J. S. BACH

THE WELL-TEMPERED CLAVIER, Vol. I

Willard A. Palmer, Editor

ABOUT THIS EDITION

Alfred has made every effort to make this book not only attractive but more useful and long-lasting as well. Usually, large books do not lie flat or stay open on the music rack. In addition, the pages (which are glued together) tend to break away from the spine after repeated use.

In this edition, pages are sewn together in multiples of 16. This special process prevents pages from falling out of the book while allowing it to stay open for ease in playing. We hope this unique binding will give you added pleasure and additional use.

Cover Painting: *by Johann Ernst Rensch, ca.1715.*
Believed to be of J. S. Bach at age 30.
Archiv für Kunst und Geschichte, Berlin.

Alfred Publishing Co., Inc.
16380 Roscoe Blvd., P.O. Box 10003
Van Nuys, CA 91410-0003

Library of Congress Cataloging in Publication Data

Bach, Johann Sebastian, 1685-1750
    The well-tempered clavier, vol. 1

    For harpsichord or piano.
    1. Preludes, fugues. (Harpsichord) 2. Preludes,
fugues. (Piano) I. Palmer, Willard A. II. Title
M.22.B11W658   80-39956
ISBN 0-88284-120-3

J. S. BACH

THE WELL-TEMPERED CLAVIER, Vol. I

This picture, the work of Johann Ernst Rentsch, the elder, is housed at the Town Museum at Erfurt. Although its authenticity has been questioned, many believe that it is a portrait of the young Johann Sebastian Bach.

Edited from all of the important sources, including J. S. Bach's Autograph Manuscript and the manuscripts of his students, relatives and personal friends. The music is newly engraved with open spacing in *dark print*, with editorial suggestions added in *lighter print*.

Willard A. Palmer, Editor

Contents

THEMATIC INDEX

THE WELL-TEMPERED CLAVIER, VOL. 1

The title page of this work, seen in the facsimile at the right in J. S. Bach's own graceful handwriting, reads as follows:

THE WELL-TEMPERED CLAVIER
or

Preludes and fugues through all the tones and semitones both as regards the major third or Ut Re Mi and as concerns the minor third of Re Mi Fa. For the profit and use of the musical youth desirous of learning, as well as for the special pastime of those who are already skilled in this study. Composed and written down by Johann Sebastian Bach, p.t. [pro tempore] Capellmeister to His Serene Highness, the Prince of Anhalt-Cöthen and Director of His Chamber Music. Anno 1722.

The term *Clavier*, as used by Bach, simply means "keyboard." In Bach's day the word was used as a general term that included clavichords, harpsichords and organs and did not exclude any of the other various keyboard instruments such as the ancient *regal* or the newly invented *fortepiano*.

The words *Well-Tempered* refer to a system of tempering (altering) the tuning of certain ones of the 12 semitones of each octave to allow the acceptable performance of music in each of the 12 major and 12 minor keys. *Meantone temperament*, the system in general used before the adoption of *well-temperament*, favored certain specific keys. A sharp could not function as a flat, and vice-versa. The use of the more remote key-signatures, or modulation to remote keys during the course of a composition, produced combinations of tones so out of tune as to be unacceptable to the ear. *Meantone temperament* is actually more in tune in the keys it favors than our present system is in any key. The *well-tempered* system preserved this feature as much as practical, compromising mainly in the tuning of the sharps and/or flats. Many modern dictionaries define *well-temperament* as *equal temperament* (an adjustment of tuning in which the octave is divided into 12 equidistant semitones). Even the late Hermann Keller, a highly respected Bach scholar, believed them to be the same. *Well-temperament*, however, is an *unequal temperament*. Its retention of the basic characteristics of the meantone system, while allowing the keys used as sharps to also serve as flats, preserves the individual tonal coloration of each of the 12 major and 12 minor keys. Most present-day listeners have only heard the preludes and fugues in this book played in *equal temperament*, since this is the standard system in use today. This system is successful in making it totally practical to play in any key, but the various keys are considerably robbed of any individuality. In *equal temperament*, all intervals except the octave are slightly out of tune. In *well-temperament* only three to five tones within the octave are tempered. For clarification of these and other points, Owen Jorgensen's excellent and ex-

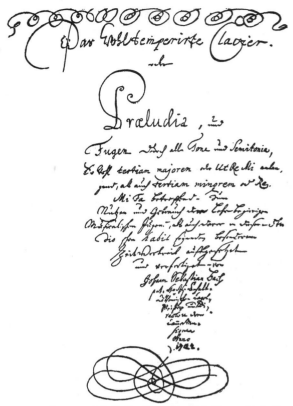

Title page of J. S. Bach's Autograph Manuscript of
The Well-Tempered Clavier, Vol. 1

haustive study, *Tuning the Historical Temperaments by Ear*, published by the Northern Michigan University Press, Marquette, 1977, is highly recommended.

As early as 1691, Andreas Werckmeister, a German organist and organ-builder, had published a work bearing the title, *Musicalische Temperatur, oder deutlicher und wahrer mathematischer Unterricht, wie man ein Clavier, sonderlich die Orgelwerke, Positive, Regale, Spinetten und dergl. wohltemperiert stimmen könne. . . "Musical Temperament, or clear and correct mathematical instruction on how one may tune a clavier, particularly organs, positives, regals, spinets and similar instruments in well-temperament."* The discovery of this system of tuning opened new territories to composers. Pachelbel wrote keyboard suites using seventeen keys. In 1704 J. K. F. Fischer, in his *Ariadne musica*, presented preludes and fugues for organ in nineteen major and minor keys, plus the *Phrygian mode* on E. Johann Mattheson used all 24 keys in a series of figured bass studies for organ in 1719. But J. S. Bach, when he wrote the first volume of *The Well-Tempered Clavier* in 1722, presented for the first time actual pieces for performance in all 24 major and minor keys.

Bach's explanation, on the title page, of major and minor intervals in terms of the scale degrees *Ut, Re, Mi, & Fa*, was necessitated by the fact that the terms *major mode* and *minor mode* were not yet generally known.

When Bach composed his *INVENTIONS & SIN-FONIAS*, completed around 1720 and revised in 1723, he used 8 major and 7 minor keys; all that the older system of tuning could acceptably accommodate. These pieces may be said to summarize the possibilities of meantone temperament, while *THE WELL-TEMPERED CLAVIER* looks forward to the greater possibilities of systems compatible to any and all keys.

In the 19th century, with the increased use of chromaticism, the well-tempered system gave way to the presently standard system of equal temperament necessary for the performance of the music of Chopin, Liszt, Wagner, Schoenberg and most 20th century composers.

WHY A NEW EDITION?

The success of the Alfred Masterwork edition of J. S. Bach's *INVENTIONS & SINFONIAS*, first published in 1968, brought immediate requests for a similar edition of *THE WELL-TEMPERED CLAVIER*. The research and preparation of this edition was begun almost immediately, and consumed a vast amount of time almost each day for about 10 years. Aside from the need for an edition showing a proper performance of each ornament, with all editorial suggestions clearly distinguished from the original text, the need for a more authentic text soon became apparent.

The popular belief that an "Urtext" edition is a flawless reproduction of the composer's original text is nowhere more false than in the case of Bach's *Well-Tempered Clavier*. The only existing near-complete copy in Bach's own handwriting is dated 1732, ten years after the original version of 1722 was completed. The editors of the Wiener "Urtext" have suggested that this Autograph Manuscript may have been written in 1722 (the date on the title page) and amended by Bach in 1732, when the latter date was added at the end of the final fugue. Some scholars have regarded the 1722 Autograph as lost. The existing Autograph contains a number of erasures and alterations, and some of these seem to have been Bach's own improvements. Some early copies made by students and relatives of Bach apparently contain notes pre-dating these revisions. These versions, in many cases, may be dimly discerned under the erasures in the Autograph. Later manuscripts from the Bach circle agree, more or less, with the revisions. It is important, of course, to check each significant source to see if the authenticity of each of these alterations may be established.

It should be noted that the three most scholarly editions of the 19th century (Kroll's edition for C. F. Peters, the same editor's later edition for the Bach-Gesellschaft, and Bischoff's edition for Steingräber, now reprinted by Kalmus) were all in disagreement on many small but significant details. Also in disagreement with all of these are the Kreutz "Urtext" (Peters), the Irmer "Urtext" (Henle), and the Dehnard/Kraus or Wiener "Urtext." Moreover, the three "Urtexts" are not in total agreement! The well-known Tovey edition, admittedly prepared from the Kroll and Bischoff editions together with the supplementary findings of the Bach-Gesellschaft, does not agree 100% with any of the above. The reasons for such differences in the work of sincere and diligent scholars demand thorough investigation.

The need for the present edition is made more acute by the fact that the Czerny, Busoni, and Hughes editions are, at this writing, still used by more teachers and more performers than the vastly superior editions previously mentioned. Many still believe that the slurs, dynamic indications, etc., in these editions are Bach's own, and that they should all be meticulously observed. Therein lies the error of using editions that make no distinction between an editor's indications and those of the composer! Furthermore, many of the editorial additions contained in the three above-mentioned editions are totally contrary to correct baroque performance practices.

The preparation of the present edition includes a painstaking investigation of how the composer may have intended these works to be performed. The editorial suggestions in print lighter than Bach's own text are the results of such a careful study. While the editor makes no claim that these suggestions represent the only correct manner in which these works may be acceptably played, they do, in our opinion, present at least one acceptable way of performing them. They will serve, at least, as a point of departure for the kind of individual freedom that was expected of every performer during Bach's day, within the bounds of good taste and with respect for certain rules of performance practice. Additional suggestions in the footnotes and in the tables compiled from various recordings will point the way to alternate solutions regarding phrasing, articulation, etc.

The most important claim that can be made for this new edition is that the text in dark print is the most accurate and authentic representation of J. S. Bach's own Autograph Manuscript that has been published to date. A careful reading of the following pages will reveal why this is true.

THE SOURCES

The Well-Tempered Clavier was not published until over 50 years after Bach's death. The only sources of authentic information are the composer's own Autograph Manuscript and the copies made by his close friends, relatives, students and their pupils.

1. *The Autograph Manuscript, P*415.* This, the primary source for our main text in dark print, is the only known copy of the 1st volume in J. S. Bach's own hand. This has already been described on page 4, in the second paragraph under "Why a New Edition." This manuscript is complete except for one missing page (2 sides) which contained *Fugue No. 13 in F♯ Major* and the first 6 measures of *Prelude No. 14 in F♯ Minor.* The manuscript is somewhat faded, due to its age. Unfortunately it suffered rather severe water damage during a flooding of the Danube River in the 1840's. There are some erasures and a number of alterations, which may not all be in J. S. Bach's own hand. It is usually possible to determine, more or less, what the text was before it was altered. This manuscript is often referred to as "The Wagner-Volkmann Autograph," after the names of two of its previous owners.

2. *The Anna Magdalena Bach Manuscript, P202.* This important manuscript was believed for many years to be an autograph. It was first sold by J. S. Bach's eldest son, Wilhelm Friedemann, to an organist named Müller, thus it came to be known as "The Müller Autograph." Some opening and closing pages were missing, and the rest of the manuscript was ultimately proven to be in the hand of J. S. Bach's second wife, Anna Magdalena. The opening pages, through measure 50 of Fugue No. 4 in C♯ Minor, were completed with considerable care, perhaps by Müller. The closing pages, beginning with measure 69 of *Fugue No. 20 in A Minor,* were completed in 1739 by one of Bach's students, J. F. Agricola. Each copyist apparently consulted Bach's unaltered autograph, or some copy of it. In our notes we refer to the first part of this manuscript simply as "P202." The portion in the hand of Bach's wife is called "The Anna Magdalena Bach Ms." The closing section is designated as "The Agricola Ms."

3. *The Walther Manuscript, P1074.* This very neat copy is in the hand of J. S. Bach's cousin and very close friend, Johann Gottfried Walther (1684-1748). It contains versions that pre-date the erasures and alterations now found in the Autograph Ms. and a few interesting variants that are worth noting.

4. *The Gerber Manuscript,* from the Riemen-schneider estate. In this manuscript Preludes and Fugues Nos. 1 through 18 are in the hand of Heinrich Nicolaus Gerber (1702-1775), who studied the 1st volume of *The Well-Tempered Clavier* with J. S. Bach in 1725. It seems likely that it was copied directly from the unaltered Autograph. Preludes and Fugues 3 through 6 are missing, and the final pages, beginning with the 19th Prelude, are in a different hand-writing. Although the calligraphy is interesting and in some cases even beautiful, there seem to be many careless errors, particularly in the pages copied by someone other than Gerber. This important copy was not used in the preparation of the Kreutz and Henle "Urtexts."

5. *The "Fischhof" Manuscript, P401.* This copy was formerly believed to be an autograph. It is an early 18th century manuscript in an unknown hand, named for one of its former owners. It bears the name of another owner, "Joh. Chr. Oley, Bernburg." It contains the early versions.

6. *The Clavier-Büchlein vor Wilhelm Friedemann Bach,* owned by Yale University School of Music. This contains the very earliest forms of 11 of the Preludes, in the following order: *No. 1 in C Major, No. 2 in C Minor, No. 6 in D Minor, No. 5 in D Major, No. 10 in E Minor, No. 9 in E Major, No. 11 in F Major, No. 3 in C♯ Major, No. 4 in C♯ Minor, No. 8 in E♭ Minor, and No. 12 in F Minor.* These are all in the hand of J. S. Bach's eldest son, Wilhelm Friedemann (1710-1784), with occasional small contributions and corrections by the father. Some are in abbreviated form, and four of them are not complete.

7. *The Notebook for Anna Magdalena (1725) P225.* This contains only one selection from *The Well-Tempered Clavier: Prelude No. 1 in C Major.* It is in the hand of J. S. Bach's second wife, Anna Magdalena.

8. *The Altnikol Manuscript, P402.* This important and exceptionally legible copy is in the hand of J. S. Bach's son-in-law, Johann Christian Altnikol. It contains the final versions.

9. *The Kirnberger Manuscript, P57.* This manuscript is from the estate of J. S. Bach's pupil, the famed musician and theoretician, Johann Philipp Kirnberger (1721-1783), and is presumably in his handwriting. This is a very legible copy, containing the final versions, with a few noteworthy variants.

*"P" identifies manuscripts from the Staatsbibliothek (Preussischer Kulturbesitz), Musikabteilung, Berlin.

10. *The Schwencke Manuscript, P203*. This is in the hand of Christian Friedrich Gottlieb Schwencke (1767-1822), a pupil of Kirnberger and Marpurg, and a close friend of Carl Philipp Emanuel Bach. Schwencke's investigations are important because he was the editor of the first edition of the 1st volume of *The Well-Tempered Clavier*, published around 1808 by Simrock (almost simultaneously with a very inferior edition published by Nägeli).

11. *The Schwencke Manuscript, P417*. This copy is said to have been written by the same person as P203, although its appearance is quite different. In any case it is an important copy, since it contains what appears to be a study of the original and the final versions. There are footnotes carefully itemizing Kirnberger's variants.

12. *The Forkel Manuscript, P212*. This incomplete manuscript, probably the least important of our sources, is in the hand of Johann Nicolaus Forkel (1749-1818). He was a friend of J. S. Bach's sons, Carl Philipp Emanuel and Wilhelm Friedemann. He wrote the first biography of J. S. Bach in 1802, gathering his information from letters and interviews from Bach's living relatives and acquaintances. His manuscript contains many variants and abbreviated versions. Forkel edited one of the earliest editions of the 1st volume of the *The Well-Tempered Clavier* for Hoffmeister & Co. around 1802. Some of the strange variants found in Czerny's edition are based on the Forkel manuscript and/or his edition for Hoffmeister.

SAMPLE RESEARCH WORKSHEETS

The facsimiles below show the preliminary research tabulations of the variants, discrepancies, etc., found in the above manuscripts for just one of the preludes. The penned notations were made by Willard Palmer's highly skilled colleague and assistant, Judith Schneider, on copies from the Bach-Gesellschaft edition. How this information was used will be explained on the following page.

Abbreviations used in the tabulations: Sch. = Schwencke; Anna = The Anna Magdalena Bach MS, P202; Cl B = Clavier-Büchlein for W. F. Bach; msg. = "missing."
The rest are self-explanatory.

HOW THE BASIC TEXT WAS PREPARED

As the research worksheets were being prepared for the entire volume, the basic text which appears in dark print in this edition was copied directly from J. S. Bach's Autograph Manuscript. This text was then carefully checked against the Czerny, Busoni, Hughes, Bischoff, Kroll (Peters), Kroll (Bach-Gesellschaft), Kreutz (Peters), Irmer (Henle), and Dehnard/ Kraus (Wiener "Urtext") editions, and all differences were tabulated. The Mugellini and Bartok editions were also examined, but only for information to be used in the metronome tables in the back of this book. All available editor's reports and lists of variants, such as those in the supplements of the Bach-Gesellschaft, and those in various treatises and essays, both in English and in German, were carefully consulted. Information derived from these and from our tabulations from the manuscripts previously listed was carefully sifted and evaluated. Obviously not all minute variants or discrepancies are significant. If, for example, a tie is missing in just one or two of the least important of the manuscripts, but is present in all of the others including the Autograph, the authenticity of that tie is not questioned. If all such trivial information had been reported, the result would have been an expensive and unwieldy volume consisting mostly of footnotes. If, on the other hand, the variant was derived from one or more of the very important sources, such as the manuscript of Anna Magdalena Bach, it was duly reported. When most of the earliest sources contained identical variants, the Autograph was carefully checked to see if similar notes were even dimly visible under the later "corrections." When they were, this was considered as evidence of the existence of an "earlier version" that had Bach's approval, at least at one time.

FUGUE NO. 1 — TWO VERSIONS

In the case of *Fugue No. 1 in C Major,* no one has disputed the fact that in the original version the subject was as follows:

A dot was later added after the fourth note, and an additional beam to the two notes following:

It is clear that the Autograph once contained the first version, which is also found in four of the earliest manuscripts mentioned in our list of sources (see the first footnote on p. 36).

Which version is correct? Perhaps both? Tovey's opinion was that the addition of the dot "improved the counterpoint everywhere." But Tovey must not have known that some of the counterpoint had to be altered when the dot was added! (See footnote ⓓ on page 33.) Not everyone has agreed that the addition of the dot improved this fugue. Wanda Landowska refused to play the dotted version, calling it "absolutely foreign" to Bach's fugal style. She blamed Kirnberger or Altnikol for making these changes, saying that they may have been "under the influence of the gallant style that flourished in their time." Of course it is impossible to positively identify anyone's handwriting from an added dot and short beam. Since there seem to be virtues in both readings, the present edition contains, published here for the first time, both versions of this fugue.

FUGUE NO. 6 — WEDGES OR DOTS?

A point of error in the Kreutz and Henle "Urtexts" occurs in *Fugue No. 6 in D Minor.* In each case they have a wedge-shaped staccato indication (▾) over the 10th note of the subject. Hermann Keller describes it as a *scharfer Keil* ("sharp wedge"). Actually it is definitely a staccato dot (•), as the following facsimile from Bach's Autograph Ms. clearly shows:

The dot, as written by Bach, usually looked more like a horizontal stroke than a vertical one. In the following example, in measure 12 of the same fugue, note the shape of the dot after the half note. Note also a very ROUND dot over the b♭ in the lower voice!

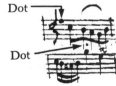

If Bach wrote dots instead of wedges, then our edition must have dots, of course. Whether dots or wedges indicate a different manner of performance is not the question here. We do know, however, that these notes are not intended to be played with an extremely short staccato touch.

OTHER PROBLEMS

The foregoing paragraphs describe our methods of dealing with the many questions that abound throughout this work, with regard to the determination of an accurate text. As other such problems occur, they are described and discussed in the footnotes.

THE PRELUDES

No particular formal restrictions are imposed by the title *Prelude*. In the case of *The Well-Tempered Clavier*, the composer's only requirement was that each prelude must be in the same key as the following fugue, and that each should prepare the listener's ear and mind for the fugue it serves to introduce. In Bach's hands, this freedom of form has resulted in an astonishing variety of preludes.

One of the oldest types of prelude, frequently used by performers as a simple "warm-up" before launching into a more difficult selection, was simply a series of broken chords constructed or improvised around a pleasing harmonic progression, perhaps with a cadenza-like flourish at the end. *Prelude No. 1 in C Major* is such a work. The flourish at the end is missing in the more primitive version found in the *Clavier-Büchlein vor W. F. Bach*, in which many of these preludes first appeared as independent pieces. J. S. Bach revised and improved most of these when he reorganized them for inclusion in *The Well-Tempered Clavier*. A number of other preludes from this work are also based on broken chords but are entirely different in their "Affekt" (emotional or expressive content). These include the brilliant *Prelude No. 2 in C♯ Major* and the elegant *No. 6 in D Minor*, which was described by Landowska as "tempestuous," by Keller as "delicately restrained," and by Tovey as "impassioned." The exuberant *Prelude No. 15 in G Major* is also basically constructed from broken chords. *No. 21 in Bb Major*, the shortest but perhaps the most brilliant prelude in this volume, combines broken chords, cadenza-like scale passages, and clusters of massive chords in

punctuated, dotted rhythm and may be considered a virtuoso *toccata*, or even a miniature *fantasia*.

Prelude No. 9 in E Major is a *pastorale*, in character or *Affekt* not unlike those of Handel's *Messiah* and Bach's own *Christmas Oratorio*. *No. 4 in C♯ Minor*, *No. 17 in G Minor* and the first part of *No. 10 in E Minor* are among those with expressive cantabile melodies, supported by various types of accompaniment. The same group may include *No. 8 in Eb Minor*, which Keller called "the first *nocturne* in keyboard music."

No. 18 in G♯ Minor, *No. 19 in A Major*, and *No. 23 in B Major* are three-part inventions. The festive *No. 17 in Ab Major* has been likened to a small baroque concerto, while *No. 24 in B Minor*, in binary form with repeated sections, resembles a baroque *sonata*. But perhaps the most surprising of all is *Prelude No. 7 in Eb Major*. It is actually a short prelude and double fugue in itself! It is not the first work of this period entitled *Praeludium* that ends with a self-contained fugue. But what has surprised (and dismayed) some commentators is that it serves to introduce another fugue of completely contrasting character!

By including such a great variety of preludes in this work, J. S. Bach has given us more insight into the many types of composition that the freedom of form permitted under the title *Praeludium* could inspire. At the same time, each of these preludes is so constructed as to perfectly fulfill its special function as an effective introduction for the following fugue.

THE UNITY OF PRELUDE AND FUGUE

It has already been mentioned that some of the preludes had their beginnings as individual pieces in the *Clavier-Büchlein vor Wilhelm Friedemann Bach*. There is evidence that two of these, the *Prelude in E Minor* (in an elementary form) and the *Prelude in E Major*, were meant to be performed as a pair. When he included the *E Minor* prelude as *No. 10* in this volume of *The Well-Tempered Clavier*, J. S. Bach vastly improved and enlarged it, so it could now stand on its own. It also was made to provide a much better introduction to the fugue that follows. A flowing, ornamented melody was added above the version in the *Clavier-Büchlein*, which now served only as its accompaniment. A second section, marked *presto*, was added, doubling the tempo and repeating the bass configurations of the first section with both hands. This exciting ending makes an appropriate introduction to the brilliant fugue with which it is paired.

While it is certain that each prelude and each fugue is complete in itself, and that any one of them may be acceptably and effectively performed individually, it is also true that when the preludes and fugues are paired, a more perfect unity is achieved through the complementary effect each has on its companion. This is not always achieved by easily perceived thematic relationships between each prelude and fugue, although some scholars have attempted to show that such relationships, however tenuous, exist in each case. Unity is often achieved through similarities in mood or *Affekt*, or in style and tempo. Strangely enough, it is possible even to achieve unity through contrast, a fact discovered by those composers who developed the classical *sonata* form. An example of this is found in the case of *No. 7 in Eb Major*. Since the prelude is actually a complete prelude and fugue in itself, it could scarcely be effectively followed by another fugue of similar character. Bach chose the only alternative available to him, following the somewhat somber prelude with a fugue constructed on a light and jovial subject. Busoni took such exception to this that in his edition he substituted the Eb Major fugue from the 2nd volume for this one. Similarly, he exchanged the two fugues in G Major, believing his judgment about their relationships to the previous preludes to be better than Bach's. These barbarous acts did nothing to improve these masterpieces, with respect to the effectiveness of the pairing or anything else.

One particular case needs a brief comment. *Prelude No. 8* is in Eb Minor, but its companion *Fugue No. 8* is in the equivalent enharmonic key, D♯ Minor. It is incredible that this disturbed Hermann Keller to the extent that he remarked "the difference of keys almost destroys the unity of the prelude and the fugue." Can any listener possibly discern the difference in these enharmonic keys? Bach certainly did this deliberately to show that

these keys, on a "well-tempered keyboard" are not only both quite practical, but are indeed one and the same. Keller then states that he will not discuss the *D♯ Minor Fugue,* but rather the *"Eb Minor Fugue!"* In many editions this fugue is transposed to the key of Eb Minor. We have retained it in the key in which the composer wrote it, and as it appears in the Autograph and ALL of the other manuscripts used as sources.

From an aesthetic point of view, it is hardly necessary to analyze the reasons each prelude and its fugue fit so admirably together. Such a study is undoubtedly interesting and profitable, but a detailed analysis requires volumes and is beyond the scope of this book. When one becomes thoroughly familiar with these works, as every keyboardist should, each fugue seems to follow its own prelude as inevitably as the night follows the day, completing and complementing it, as the two merge into a perfectly unified whole.

THE FUGUES

The fugue, strictly speaking, is not a "form." Instead, it is a procedure for employing a special type of theme in a continually developing contrapuntal texture. This is done through the use of a number of devices, many of which are completely optional. None of Bach's fugues fits the rules for fugue-writing outlined in early textbooks, and many modern textbooks hesitate to use his fugues as examples, since none of them follows precisely the same procedure.

In a fugue, there are usually a fixed number of melodic strands, which, due to the choral origin of the fugue, are called "voices." To each fugue in *The Well-Tempered Clavier,* Bach gave the title *FUGA,* which in Italian, means "flight." The name was probably derived from the way each voice "flies" after the preceding one when it enters. In the titles, Bach also specified the number of voices in each fugue. In the title *FUGA 1 a 4,* the *a 4* is an abbreviation for *a 4 VOCI,* meaning, in Italian, "in 4 voices." In this volume there are one fugue in 2 voices, eleven in 3, ten in 4, and two in 5 voices.

A fugue begins as the 1st voice states the theme in the tonic of the key. This first statement is called the *SUBJECT* or *dux* (leader). The 2nd voice then enters, stating the same theme, usually in the dominant of the key. This is called the *ANSWER* or *comes* (companion). While the answer is in progress, the 1st voice continues with a melody that ideally moves "counter" to the theme. If this bit of counterpoint is used with each entry, and perhaps also in later measures of the fugue, it merits the name *COUNTERSUBJECT.* In *Fugue No. 2 in C Minor,*

in three voices (p. 42), the first two voices enter as follows:

Any portion of a fugue in which each voice enters in its turn is called an *EXPOSITION.* In the example above, the exposition is not yet a *COMPLETE EXPOSITION,* because only 2 of the 3 voices have entered.

After all the voices have entered, it is customary for the fugue to continue with something different from subject and answer. Often a short motive, which may be derived from the material previously heard, is developed in a sequence, to make what is known as an *EPISODE.* An episode may even occur before the exposition is complete, and that is precisely what happens in this fugue. It continues as shown below, with an episode in which the upper voice is heard in a sequence built on the motive of the first 5 notes of the subject. Against this, the other voice continues with notes derived by inverting the first part of the countersubject. This episode serves to lead to the entrance of the 3rd voice, and with the 1st bass note of measure 9, the exposition is complete.

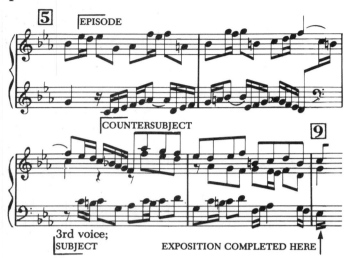

Note that, as the 3rd voice enters with its restatement of the subject, the upper voice continues with the countersubject. The inner voices drop out momentarily, with the result that the entry of the 3rd voice is made very clear to the listener. Both upper voices then continue, using material mostly derived from the 2nd part of the countersubject.

After the first exposition is complete, most fugues continue with a series of episodes and additional partial or complete expositions. Some episodes modulate so as to lead to an exposition in some related key. The original key returns, of course, at the end, and often the fugue closes with a final complete exposition. Some theorists call this final exposition the *RECAPITULATION*.

The fugue we have been discussing is, after the exposition, mostly a series of episodes, leading to a statement of the subject in only one voice, and continuing with another episode. There is no complete exposition at the end. In measure 26, Bach brings in the bass voice at its lowest possible pitch. After the complete subject is heard in the bass, there is a dramatic interruption of all three voices simultaneously. (See the 3 eighth rests near the end of measure 28.) The voices return together with what sounds very much like a final cadence. But Bach surprises us by extending the fugue with a particularly effective *CODA*. The subject is sounded again by the upper voice. Extra notes are added to the inner part for stronger support, and against all this the bass sustains its final tonic note, strengthened by the addition of the lower octave through to the end. Such a sustained tone is called *PEDAL POINT*, the term being derived from the fact that such notes are frequently found in organ fugues, usually sustained on the pedal keyboard. The pedal

point, usually on the tonic or dominant tone, is an important fugal device. It serves to increase tension and excitement in some cases, majesty and dignity in others, as the bass maintains its one tone insistently, regardless of what may occur in the other voices.

—PEDAL POINT CONTINUES—

OTHER FUGAL DEVICES

In *Fugue No. 1 in C Major* (p. 32), the voices first enter 1½ measures apart:

After the 4 voices enter to complete the exposition, no episode is used. Instead, beginning in measure 7, the subject is heard again, this time in the soprano voice, and the tenor voice quickly follows with the answer, only one beat behind. This "drawing together" of the subject and answer is called *STRETTO*:

The Italian word *stretto* meaning "narrow" or "drawn together," is often used as a noun to refer to a section of a fugue in which the device is used; thus the above measures may be called "a *stretto*." The plural is *stretti*.

In the same fugue there are many stretti. In the following example (measures 14 & 15) all 4 voices are used in stretto. The interval of time is not the same between all entrances of the subject and answers, but each voice is overlapped. In this example a separate staff is used for each voice, to show the entrances more clearly:

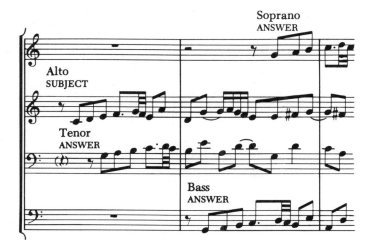

A particularly remarkable stretto is found in *Fugue No. 22 in B♭ Minor*, beginning in measure 67 (see p. 191). All 5 voices are heard in stretto at a distance of a half-note apart:

INVERSION is an especially important fugal device, frequently used in *The Well-Tempered Clavier*. Any melodic idea, such as a subject or countersubject may be inverted by reversing every interval, descending instead of ascending, and vice-versa. The result is a new melody, very much related to the original one, and complementary to it. An ex-

cellent example is found in *Fugue No. 20 in A Minor*. The inversion begins in measure 14 (p. 173). Here we show only half of the very long subject:

Another effective fugal device is *AUGMENTATION*. The values of the notes of the original melody are increased (often doubled). The opposite effect, *DIMINUTION*, is not so frequently found in Bach's fugues. Augmentation adds a certain dignity, as well as a climactic effect, particularly when it is applied to the subject of a fugue. This example is from *Fugue No. 8 in D♯ Minor*, which begins on page 92:

The following augmentation is found beginning in measure 77 (p. 96):

In this same fugue, beginning in measure 61 (p. 95), the devices of *AUGMENTATION*, *STRETTO*, and *INVERSION* are ingeniously combined:

Some fugues, such as *No. 1 in C Major, No. 8 in D♯ Minor,* and *No. 22 in B♭ Minor,* have no episodes, but depend on the other fugal devices mentioned, particularly stretto, for their development. Such fugues are called *STRETTO - FUGUES.*

DOUBLE AND TRIPLE FUGUES

A fugue with two subjects is called a *DOUBLE FUGUE.* The two subjects may be stated together at the beginning of the fugue, or the 1st subject may be developed alone, to be joined later by the 2nd subject. Remarkably, none of the pieces entitled *FUGA* in the 1st volume is a double fugue, but there is a double fugue contained in one of the pieces entitled *PRAELUDIUM.* See *Prelude No. 7 in E♭ Major,* beginning on page 79. The first 10 measures constitute a short toccata-like introduction. Measures 11-24 serve as a transition section in which a motive derived from the 1st subject of the coming fugue is developed in stretto, then joined with short motives from the 2nd subject. The *DOUBLE FUGUE* begins in measure 25, page 80, as both subjects are heard simultaneously;

Fugue No. 4 in C♯ Minor, found in this book beginning on page 63, has 3 subjects, and thus may be called a *TRIPLE FUGUE.* Note the contrasting character of the subjects:

In the opening measures, the 1st subject is heard alone. The remaining 4 voices are added in complete exposition. In measure 35, the 2nd subject is heard against the 1st subject. In measure 49, the melody of the 3rd subject makes its first appearance. The following excerpt, beginning in measure 73, shows an example of how the 3 subjects are used together. Observe here a very short example of *DIMINUTION,* applied to the first 3 notes of the 2nd subject:

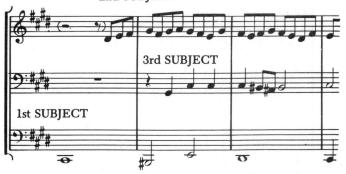

In measures 94-97, stretti on the themes of the 1st and 3rd subjects occur simultaneously. In this example, some contrapuntal notes are omitted for clarity:

J. S. BACH, MASTER OF THE FUGUE

The almost incredible musical and contrapuntal skill of J. S. Bach, as evidenced in the above isolated examples, becomes increasingly astounding to us when the complete fugues are further explored. That Bach was truly the great master of the contrapuntal art is further revealed to us in a comment written by his most illustrious son, Carl Philipp Emanuel, in a letter to Bach's first biographer, Johann Nicolaus Forkel:

> *He could tell you, immediately upon hearing the first entry of a fugue subject, exactly what contrapuntal devices it would be possible to apply, and which of these the composer should feel obligated to use. On such occasions, when I was standing next to him and he had made such observations, he would joyfully nudge me when his expectations were fulfilled.*

AWARENESS OF
FUGAL STRUCTURE IMPORTANT

The performer who is aware of the structural principles of fugues, and who is always conscious of each fugal device as it occurs, will inevitably play them with more understanding, and the performance will always be more convincing and effective than that of the performer who merely is content to play the notes, however expressively that performer may strive to play them. The sections and devices of the fugues are not difficult to identify, and the conscientious student is urged to be constantly alert and studiously analytical when learning these works.

ORNAMENTATION

The following table of ornaments, headed *Explication unterschiedlicher Zeichen, so gewisse Manieren artig zu spielen, andeuten* (Explanation of various signs, showing how to play certain ornaments correctly), was prepared by J. S. Bach, in his own handwriting, and included in the *Clavier-Büchlein*, which he prepared for his son, Wilhelm Friedemann.

The above table is reproduced below, in modern notation.

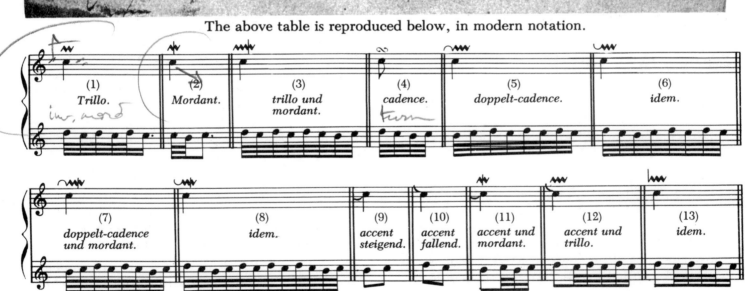

(1) Trillo.	(2) Mordant.	(3) trillo und mordant.	(4) cadence.	(5) doppelt-cadence.	(6) idem.

(7) doppelt-cadence und mordant.	(8) idem.	(9) accent steigend.	(10) accent fallend.	(11) accent und mordant.	(12) accent und trillo.	(13) idem.

Bach's own terms for these ornaments are given in the table in a mixture of Italian, French, German, and Latin. The term *idem*, meaning "the same," used in the case of ornaments 6, 8, and 13, refers to the fact that these ornaments had the same name as the previous ornament in the table, in Bach's terminology. The most common English names of the above are:

(1) Trill. (2) Mordant. (3) Trill with termination. (4) Turn. (5) Ascending trill. (6) Descending trill.

(7) Ascending trill with termination. (8) Descending trill with termination. (9) Appoggiatura from below. (10) Appoggiatura from above. (11) Appoggiatura & mordent. (12) Appoggiatura & trill. (13) The same.

The above table includes nearly all of the ornaments used in *The Well-Tempered Clavier*. The following short discussion will present a few general rules and show how they are applied to specific instances in this volume. The ornaments are discussed in the same order as they appear in the table, and a few additional ones, not included above, are also explained.

14

Since the *Explication* applies each ornament to a quarter note only, and that application is only practical at a moderate tempo, it can only show the *GENERAL CONFIGURATION* of each ornament. Note that all ornaments in the table begin *on the beat*. They are played diatonically in the keys in force at the moment they occur, with very few exceptions.

1. THE TRILL ♪♪ ♪♪♪ *tr*

These symbols are used interchangeably to indicate a long or short trill.

All trills begin on the *upper note*.

The trill may be rather freely interpreted by the performer. It may come to rest on the principal note or, at times, continue for the entire value of the note. The minimum number of notes in any trill is four.

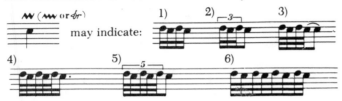

A trill is sometimes made more effective by lingering slightly on the first note.

Trills on longer notes may consume the entire value of the note or may stop on any beat or fraction of a beat.

2. THE MORDENT ♪♪

The word "mordent" is derived from the Latin *mordere*, meaning "to bite." This suggests that mordents should have an incisive quality. They contribute brilliance and sometimes serve to accentuate the rhythm. They should generally be played quite rapidly; sometimes even more quickly than these realizations show:

In extremely rapid passages, it is effective to strike both notes simultaneously, then immediately release the lower note (C. P. E. Bach, *ESSAY,** II, v, 1.).

Sometimes, on long notes, a mordent may have additional repercussions. It is then called a *LONG MORDENT*. Sometimes this is done when the ordinary mordent sign is used, but often this is indicated by the sign ♪♪♪ or ♪♪♪ . The function of the long mordent is different from that of the normal or short mordent. It fills out the value of the note.

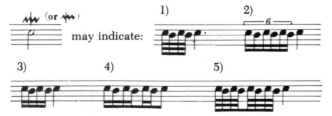

When a mordent is used to fill out a note, it cannot consume the entire value of the note. "A small portion of its original value must be left plain, since even the best used mordent sounds terrible when carried, like a trill, directly into the following note." (C. P. E. Bach, *ESSAY*, II, v, 8.) In the same work, in II, v, 11, we read, "the brilliance of a mordent is often enhanced by raising its lower note one half-step." Thus a mordent is not inevitably played diatonically.

3. THE TRILL WITH TERMINATION ♪♪♪

This is sometimes called the *TRILL WITH SUFFIX*, or the *TRILL WITH TURNED ENDING*, or less often, the *TRILL AND MORDENT*.

The *termination* consists of two closing notes, connected to the trill and generally played at the same speed as the trill repercussions.

The trill itself requires a minimum of four notes, and the termination requires two additional notes; thus the minimum number of notes in the entire ornament is six:

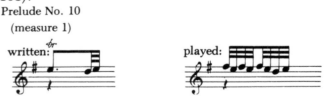

Trill

The termination is often written out in full, as it is in the 1st measure of *Prelude No. 10 in E Minor* (p. 103):

Prelude No. 10
(measure 1)

In his *ESSAY*, II, iii, 13, C. P. E. Bach comments that a trill may have an added termination when there is time, whether it is indicated or not. These are better when the trilled note ascends to the following note but may be added regardless of stepwise ascent or descent.

An example of the use of a termination with a trill indicated by the sign *tr* , in stepwise ascent, occurs in the opening measures of *Fugue No. 6 in D Minor* (p. 76), in the statement of the subject.

Fugue No. 6
(measure 1-3)

the trill and the following note are played:

*C. P. E. Bach, *Versuch über die wahre Art das Clavier zu spielen* (Essay on the True Art of Keyboard Playing), Berlin 1753.

In measures 28 & 29, the subject is repeated in the alto voice. Here Bach has marked the very same trill-ed note . It is performed the same in both instances, of course.

This fugue has many more examples of this ornament. Refer to pages 76-78.

In *Prelude No. 18 in G♯ Minor*, in measure 13 (p. 156) there is a trill of sufficient length to use a termination, regardless of its stepwise descent.

Prelude No. 18
(measure 13)

4. THE TURN ∾

In his manuscripts, J. S. Bach used a vertical or sloping sign for the turn: ?

The turn in Bach's music always begins on the note *above* the principal note.

In his *ESSAY*, II, iv, 3, C. P. E. Bach says "The turn is almost always performed rapidly." He gives the following examples:

According to the section of C. P. E. Bach's *ESSAY* just cited, the turn is a miniature suffixed trill, in effect, and can be used as a simplification of same.

5. THE TRILL WITH PREFIX FROM BELOW ∿

This is sometimes called the *ASCENDING TRILL*. The prefix consists of two notes; the trill requires at least four notes; thus the minimum number of notes for the entire ornament is six.

Since this ornament is usually employed on long notes, and since long trills are usually best played with a termination, this ornament, in practice, usually becomes a *TRILL WITH PREFIX FROM BELOW, WITH TERMINATION* (see No. 7, below). Like all long trills, the repercussions need not be measured. The number of repercussions will depend on the length of the note, the tempo, and the skill and taste of the performer.

6. THE TRILL WITH PREFIX FROM ABOVE ∿

This is sometimes called the *DESCENDING TRILL*. The prefix from above consists of four notes, and is similar to the turn. The trill requires at least four notes; thus the minimum number of notes for the entire ornament is eight.

In practice this ornament is usually replaced with a TRILL WITH PREFIX FROM ABOVE, WITH TERMINATION (see No. 8, below). The repercussions need not be measured.

7. THE TRILL WITH PREFIX FROM BELOW, WITH TERMINATION ∿

This is sometimes called the *ASCENDING TRILL, WITH TERMINATION* (or *SUFFIX*).

This ornament consists of three parts: the prefix, the trill, and the suffix (termination). It cannot be played with fewer than eight notes, as shown in the *Explication*:

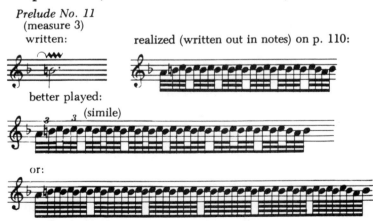

The treble ornament in *Prelude No. 11 in F Major* (p. 110), measure 3, becomes this ornament in practice, although the termination is not indicated in the sign, which is ∿ instead of ∿. (A long trill, particularly when followed by an ascending step of a 2nd, should have a termination.)

Prelude No. 11
(measure 3)

In the above case, a slow trill results in consecutive 5ths with the left hand notes, thus a faster trill is better. This is further discussed in *ABOUT CONSECUTIVES*, on p. 19.

8. THE TRILL WITH PREFIX FROM ABOVE, WITH TERMINATION

This is sometimes called the *DESCENDING TRILL, WITH TERMINATION* (or *SUFFIX*).

This ornament requires at least two notes more than the one previously discussed, thus it usually occurs only on long notes.

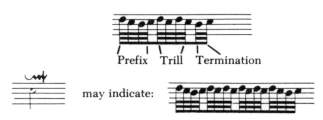

Prefix   Trill   Termination

may indicate:

The treble ornament in *Prelude No. 11 in F Major* (p. 110), measure 4, becomes this ornament in practice, although the termination is not indicated in the sign which is ⌣⌣⌣ instead of ⌣⌣⌣ .

Prelude No. 11
(measure 4)
written: realized on p. 110:

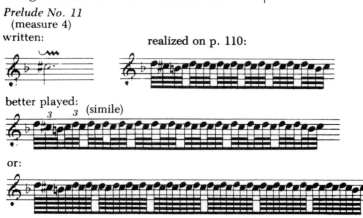

better played: (simile)

or:

9-12. THE APPOGGIATURA INDICATED BY ORNAMENT ONLY

The small hook may have been derived from the slur that is used with a small note indicating an appoggiatura.

The word "appoggiatura" is derived from the Italian *appoggiare*, meaning "to lean."

If the hook comes from below the main note, a *LOWER* or *ASCENDING APPOGGIATURA* is used. The note a diatonic step or half-step below the principal note is played on the beat of the principal note. This note receives the accent and resolves more softly to the main note. If the hook comes from above the main note, the *UPPER* or *DESCENDING APPOGGIATURA* is used. When the value of the main note is divisible by two, the appoggiatura is given half of that value:

9. Ascending Appoggiatura   *10. Descending Appoggiatura*

written: played: written: played:

An appoggiatura used with a dotted note usually receives two-thirds of the value of the principal note:

written: played: written: played:

The double hook (⟍) has the same meaning as the single hook.

An example of the double hook is found in *Prelude No. 8 in Eb Minor*, in measure 36 (see p. 91).

Prelude No. 8
(measure 36) double hook   played: appoggiatura

This ornament is notated differently in the various manuscripts used as sources. Refer to footnote ⓤ on page 91 for these interesting observations and a facsimile of this measure.

Examples 11 & 12 in the *Explication* show the appoggiatura used with the mordent or the trill. Note that in example 12, the appoggiatura becomes the starting note of the trill. (See also 13, *THE PREPARED TRILL*, which is just another way of indicating the same ornament as that shown in example 12.)

11. Appoggiatura and Mordent   *12. Appoggiatura and Trill*

written: played: written: played:

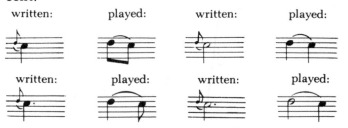

Note that in both of the above examples, the appoggiatura portion of the ornament is given its usual value, in this case, half the value of the principal note.

THE APPOGGIATURA INDICATED BY SMALL NOTES ♪♪♪♪

Most of the appoggiaturas in *THE WELL-TEMPERED CLAVIER* are written in small notes.

In playing these appoggiaturas, the same rules are observed as those outlined for the hook. All appoggiaturas are played on the beat and receive the accent.

written: played: written: played:

written: played: written: played:

13. THE PREPARED TRILL ⌣⌣⌣

J. S. Bach used the same name for this ornament as for 12, *THE APPOGGIATURA AND TRILL*. The appoggiatura is treated as a prolongation of the starting note of the trill.

written: played:

The 13 ornaments in Bach's table have been discussed. Two additional ornaments used in *THE WELL-TEMPERED CLAVIER* remain to be explained.

14. THE SCHLEIFER ⌇

This ornament may also be called the "slide." The zig-zag portion of the ornament has nothing to do with a trill or mordent but serves to mark the line or space upon which the ornament begins. When this sign is used, the two lower neighboring diatonic notes are played on the beat of the principal note and quickly slurred to the principal note:

An example of the Schleifer occurs in *Fugue No. 3 in C♯ Major*, in measure 13 (see p. 51). Like the ordinary mordent, this ornament is always played very quickly.

Fugue No. 3
(measure 13)

15. THE BAROQUE ACCIACCATURA

Acciaccatura is an Italian word meaning "crushed." The word has been applied (sometimes quite erroneously) to the modern *short appoggiatura* (♪). This would only be accurately termed an *acciaccatura* if it were literally "crushed" simultaneously with the following main note. The appoggiatura with a cross-stroke was never written by J. S. Bach, and editions containing them are not accurate.

The *BAROQUE ACCIACCATURA* appears as a cross-stroke between two chord-notes. The chord is arpeggiated, and a dissonant note is added between two chord-notes, in the place where the cross-stroke appears. The notes of the chord are held, but the added dissonant note is instantly released:

This kind of acciaccatura is especially effective on the harpsichord, but is also not without merit on the piano, and can be played with good effect on any keyboard instrument. An example may be found in *Prelude No. 4 in C♯ Minor*, in measure 29 (p. 59):

Prelude No. 4
(measure 29)

If the cross-stroke is present, the chord is arpeggiated, even if the wavy line is absent.

ABOUT THE ARPEGGIATION OF CHORDS

The practice of arpeggiating or "breaking" chords was so generally employed on the harpsichord and clavichord during Bach's day that it was not considered necessary to notate it in the music. When arpeggiation is indicated, the chord may be even more broadly spread. No chord sounds very good on the harpsichord without at least some slight degree of spreading.

Chords may be broken beginning with the top note, or beginning with the lower note, or if there is enough time in both directions, particularly in chords near the end of the piece (especially in preludes that have an improvisatory character).

While this type of arpeggiation is more effective on the harpsichord than on the piano, the pianist may feel free to employ the effect with tasteful discretion; it should not be overdone, for example, in rapid passages made up of many consecutive chords.

Prelude No. 1 in C Major is a written-out example of a prelude based on a series of broken chords, which most composers of Bach's day would have notated as plain chords, leaving the choice of configuration to the performer. Bach frequently did exactly that. In the manuscript of the *Clavier-Büchlein vor Wilhelm Friedemann Bach*, after a few bars that establish the configuration, the rest of this prelude is notated in plain chords. Thus it should be played with over-lapping notes, rapidly enough to give the effect of a series of improvised broken chords. Some performers have played the sixteenth notes in the right hand staccato. Such "fussy" playing is, in this editor's opinion, completely out of character with the baroque style and totally foreign to the composer's intentions.

MORE ABOUT THE UPPER-NOTE TRILL

In his *ESSAY*, II, iii, 1-5, C. P. E. Bach outlines 8 contexts in which trills may be used: 1) on the repetition of a note, 2) in step-wise passages, 3) in leaping passages, 4) in succession, 5) in cadences, 6) on sustained notes, 7) at fermatas, and 8) at caesuras. After listing these uses, he adds, "The trill always begins on the tone above the principal note."

Can C. P. E. Bach's principles be applied to J. S. Bach's music? In no case does C. P. E. Bach's discussion of any ornament disagree with his father's table. His discussion of their application agrees with the ways his father applies them. An example is the *APPLICATIO* and other pieces he wrote for another son, Wilhelm Friedemann, in the *Clavier-Büchlein*. The son's book can serve as a companion to the father's, and by studying the two together we become more enlightened. We see that the things

J. S. Bach taught one son were taught identically to the other. C. P. E. Bach wrote,"My father was my only teacher, and everything I know, I learned from him."

Proper baroque performance practices, along with the correct execution of baroque ornaments, have been rediscovered in the 20th century, beginning with the brilliant pioneering efforts of Arnold Dolmetsch, who revealed his findings in his still excellent book, *THE INTERPRETATION OF THE MUSIC OF THE XVII & XVIII CENTURIES, REVEALED BY CONTEMPORARY EVIDENCE* (London, 1915). Scholars such as Howard Ferguson, Thurston Dart, Michael Collins, Putnam Aldrich, Sol Babitz, David Fuller, and a host of others, have added important evidence in theses and various articles published in the scholarly journals. Arnold Dolmetsch's work has been diligently carried on by his son, Carl Dolmetsch, and by his brilliant student, Robert Donington, in his valuable book, *THE INTERPRETATION OF EARLY MUSIC* (London, 1963; newly revised and enlarged version, New York, 1973). Also important is the same author's *A PERFORMER'S GUIDE TO BAROQUE MUSIC* (New York, 1973). Through the objective studies of these and other scholars, the trill from the upper auxiliary has been firmly established as standard baroque performance practice.

In view of the knowledge we now possess, including 17th and 18th century table after table showing all simple trills beginning on the beat and on the upper note, and all prefixed trills beginning on the beat, it is amazing and annoying that we still so frequently encounter trills beginning on the main note and/or ahead of the beat, not only in recordings of famous artists, but also in lectures and articles by musicians who should know better.

In Alfred Kreutz's *BEMERKUNGEN ZUM VORTRAG* (Observations about Execution) published with his edition of *THE WELL-TEMPERED CLAVIER*, Vol. I, by C. F. Peters, he recommends that about two-thirds of the trills should begin on the main note. The reason is simply that Kreutz believes, as too many others do, that a trill preceded by an upper 2nd must begin on the main note, to avoid repeating the preceding note! This is in disagreement with all the examples we have from C. P. E. Bach, Couperin, D'Angelbert, Marpurg, Agricola, Türk, Quantz and many, many others. Not one of Bach's contemporaries has mentioned such a rule!

F. W. Marpurg, in his *ANLEITUNG, I, iv, 7, wrote, "A trill, wherever it may stand, begins with the accessory note. If the upper note, with which the trill should begin, immediately precedes the trilled note, that note must be repeated with a new attack; or before one begins the trill, it must be connected by means of a tie to the preceding note."

The upper-note trill functions melodically, harmonically, and expressively like an upper appoggiatura. Just as an upper appoggiatura is most effective when it repeats the preceding note, so is the trill most effective in the same context. In fact, the most important use of a trill is in cadences such as the following one:

The note preceding the trilled note serves as preparation for a suspension. This same note is repeated and reiterated as the upper note of the trill, and this produces the effect of suspension. The resolution occurs when the trill ends on the main note:

The lengthening of the value of the dot and shortening of the following note is explained in a subsequent section. The effectiveness of this upper-note trill may be tested by playing the same passage, beginning the trill on the principal note. The expressiveness produced by the dissonant sound of the upper note disappears. The dissonance-resolution effect is one of the most expressive sounds in music, and it represents an important function of the trill in many of its contexts.

Even in those passages where beginning the trill on the upper note does not produce such an effect, the present editor is convinced, just as Robert Donington says he is (*INTERPRETATION OF EARLY MUSIC*, pp. 632-633), that the trill was begun habitually on the upper note during this period, even when it was not particularly functional, from a harmonic standpoint, to do so.

Even as late as 1789, Daniel Gottlob Türk, in his *KLAVIERSCHULE* (Leipzig & Halle), III, 33, labels all main notes trills "incorrect." His illustrations show upper-note trills which reiterate the preceding upper 2nd, even in chains of descending 2nds. He also shows that even trills in the bass begin on the upper auxiliary.

It is hoped that those who may be skeptical will seek out these and other references which confirm the above. Most of all, it is hoped that they will at least experiment with the ornament realizations in light print, suggested by the editor, since these are based on a very careful study of 18th century performance practices, and those of the Bach circle in particular.

*Friedrich Wilhelm Marpurg, *Anleitung zum Klavierspielen* (Introduction to Keyboard Playing), Berlin, 1755.

ABOUT CONSECUTIVES (Resulting from Ornament Realizations)

Consecutive (parallel) octaves or perfect 5ths, which were forbidden in music during the baroque period, should be avoided in the realization of ornaments, if this can be done without falsifying the performance of the ornament.

1. WITH APPOGGIATURAS

Occasionally the length of an appoggiatura must be adjusted to avoid consecutives with another voice. An example is found in *Prelude No. 10 in E Minor*, in measure 9 (p. 103).

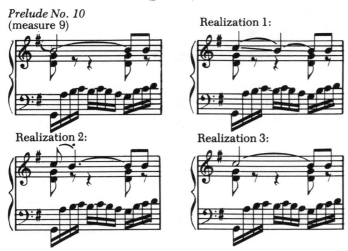

Prelude No. 10 (measure 9)

Realization 1:

Realization 2:

Realization 3:

According to the general rule, this appoggiatura should be given half the value of the following note. If the tie is included in the note's value, the appoggiatura will resolve on the 6th sixteenth of the measure. Thus the resolution would occur with the upper voice moving from C down to B as the lower voice moves from B up to C. This, of course, is no resolution at all. If the appoggiatura is played as a quarter note, as in *realization 1*, totally exposed consecutive octaves of the most offensive sort will result.

To avoid such consecutives, an appoggiatura may be shortened or lengthened. Because long appoggiaturas are more expressive than shorter ones, *realization 2* is not as effective as *realization 3*. Long appoggiaturas occurring with tied notes were frequently held for the value of the 1st of the two tied notes and resolved on the last. This was, in fact, the rule for resolving appoggiaturas on tied notes in 6/8 and 6/4 time, given by J. J. Quantz in his *ESSAY** VIII, 7ff. C. P. E. Bach, in his *ESSAY* II, ii, 16, writes, "There are occasions when an appoggiatura must be prolonged beyond its normal length, for the expressive feeling conveyed. Sometimes the length is determined by the harmony."

2. WITH TRILLS

Consecutives that arise from trill realizations should never be "solved" by beginning the trill on the main note, since that error is likely to be at least

as serious a violation of the baroque style as the consecutives. There are usually good solutions available.

In *Fugue No. 3 in C♯ Major*, in measure 38 (p. 54), the trill prefix from above is best not played as recommended in the Edwin Hughes edition (Schirmer), since it causes consecutive perfect 5ths which could otherwise be avoided.

Fugue No. 3 (measure 38)

EDWIN HUGHES' REALIZATION:

BETTER:

In this solution the prefix begins slowly and accelerates to a rapid trill, which, once the problem is passed, may be played unmeasured, if desired. This is one of the most beautiful kinds of trill, because of its improvised sound.

A similar problem, occurring in *Fugue No. 24 in B Minor*, is discussed in footnote (d) on page 200.

THE ADDITION OF ORNAMENTS

The best performance of these preludes and fugues will not always result from confining the ornamentation to that which the composer himself indicates. The evidence for this is overwhelming. Some ornaments were omitted because their addition was obvious to performers of that period. Also, it was part of what was known as "the method of playing" to add ornaments extemporaneously, carefully chosen to heighten the *Affekt* (sad, happy, majestic, etc.) of the piece. Only in the slower preludes, such as *Prelude No. 4* and *Prelude No. 8*, has Bach indicated in detail the kind of ornaments that were usually expected to be added by the performer.

*Johann Joachim Quantz, *Versuch einer Anweisung die Flöte traversiere zu spielen (Essay on a Method of Playing the Transverse Flute)*, Berlin, 1752.

1. OBLIGATORY ORNAMENTS

A trill is required in certain types of cadences, whether indicated or not. Such trills should usually end with (a) a termination (turned ending), or (b) an anticipation of the following note.

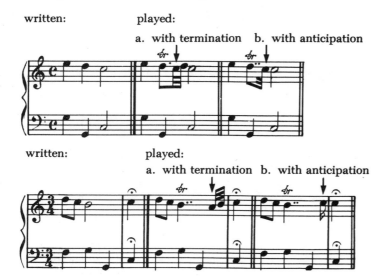

In *THE WELL-TEMPERED CLAVIER*, many cadences similar to those above occur with no ornament signs. Two typical examples may be noted in *Fugue No. 19 in A Major*. The first example, from measure 41, (p. 167), is a cadence in the relative key (F♯ minor). This trill is not indicated in Bach's Autograph Manuscript but is found in several of the other sources. (See footnote ⓘ on p. 167.)

Fugue No. 19
(measure 41)

(The lengthening of the value of the dot and shortening of its following note are part of baroque practice. This is explained under *CONVENTIONAL ALTERATIONS OF RHYTHM*, on page 22.)

The 2nd example, from the last measure of the same fugue (p. 168), has a final cadence to the tonic chord, with no trill indicated in any of the sources. It should certainly be added anyway, in performance.

Fugue No. 19
(measure 54)

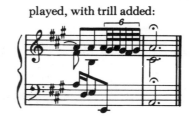

The function of such trills is to make the cadence more interesting and expressive, by adding the element of dissonance and resolution. The dissonant upper note of the trill is reiterated until it resolves on the consonant principal note. When the inner voice or voices already have a dissonance-resolution function, or when they are too busy for the trill to be effective or practical, the trill need not be added.

When a thematic idea is heard at its first appearance with an ornament, that ornament should be added at subsequent appearances of the same theme, whether or not it is indicated by the composer. This is particularly true of fugue subjects. Often the ornaments were omitted in later statements of subject and answer because the baroque performer knew they were to be added.

In *Fugue No. 7 in E♭ Major*, a trill is present on the 2nd quarter of the 2nd measure, in the statement of the fugue subject. This trill is indicated in the answer (measures 3-4) and in the next statement of the subject (measures 6-7). But when the next answer appears (measures 11-12), the trill is missing from every manuscript. It should undoubtedly be added. (See pp. 84-85.)

Fugue No. 7
(measures 1-2)

Fugue subject with indicated trill:

(measures 11-12)

Fugal answer with no trill indicated:
(only the soprano voice is given here)

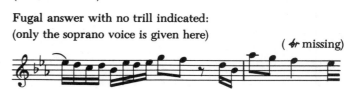

In some compositions it is quite difficult to perform all ornaments that appear in the first statement of the subject in the later measures of the work, after the counterpoint has become more intricate. *Fugue No. 23 in B Major* is a good example. Nevertheless, we can believe that Bach himself was able to accomplish this. In the first biography of Bach, Forkel wrote, "He was the perfect master of those passages in which, while some fingers perform a trill, the others of the same hand must continue playing." Concerning Bach's skill on the organ pedals, Ernest Ludwig Gerber (the son of Bach's student, H. N. Gerber) wrote, "On the pedals his feet had to imitate with perfect accuracy every theme and passage that his hands had played. No appoggiatura, no short trill was suffered to be lacking. . . . he even made long double trills with both feet. . . ."

2. IMPROVISED ORNAMENTS

The practice of adding ornaments *ex tempore* was a part of the "manner of playing" learned by every student of music during Bach's day. This was thought to be particularly necessary in repeated sections. Any musician who made a repeat without adding some appropriate embellishments was considered to be dull and unimaginative.

In *THE WELL-TEMPERED CLAVIER*, Vol. I, repeats of sections occur only in *Prelude No. 24 in B Minor.* The repeats should be observed. If they are not, the proportionate lengths of the prelude and fugue are distorted. Each section should be more elaborately embellished when it is repeated. Suggested ornaments for use on the repeats are given by the editor, in light print (see pp. 197-199). The suggested embellishments may be used or ignored, or different ornaments may be substituted at the performer's discretion.

Ornaments may also be added in appropriate places during the course of a selection that has no repeats, if they tastefully contribute to the *Affekt*. In this respect, baroque performers had far more freedom than those of the classical and romantic periods. Ornaments added to a fugue subject, however, more or less obligate the performer to add identical ones in similar places in the same theme, each time it is used as subject or answer, throughout the fugue.

It is particularly appropriate to add embellishments during the free cadenza-like sections of those preludes that have an improvisatory character, such as *No. 2 in C Minor*, or in very expressive arioso preludes such as *No. 4 in C♯ Minor.*

When a cadential trill cannot effectively be added at the end of a prelude, a mordent or an appoggiatura and mordent will often fit the context. Florid arpeggiation of the closing chords is sometimes especially effective.

The following simple rules will aid the performer in selecting ornaments appropriate to the context:

1. On ascending steps or leaps a mordent is appropriate:

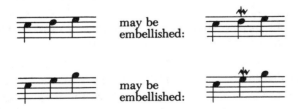

2. On ascending steps ONLY, the following are effective:

a. An ascending appoggiatura:

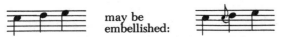

b. An ascending appoggiatura and mordent:

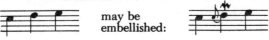

3. On descending steps or leaps, the following are appropriate:

a. A trill, long or short:

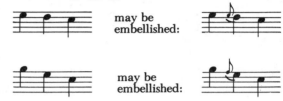

b. A descending appoggiatura:

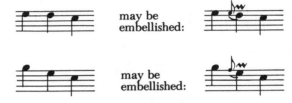

c. A descending appoggiatura and trill:

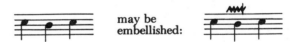

4. On melodies that descend stepwise, then ascend to the same note, a trill with termination is in good context:

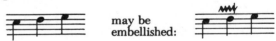

The same ornament may be used in passages ascending stepwise:

5. On repeated notes, a plain trill or mordent may be used:

EXAMPLES OF ADDED EMBELLISHMENTS:
Prelude No. 2
(last 2 counts, p. 41)

Prelude No. 6
(closing chords, p. 75)

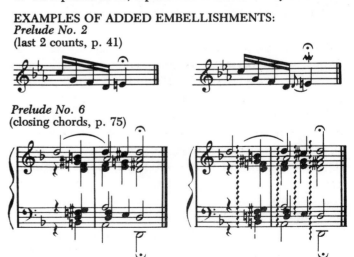

Each chord may be arpeggiated upward or downward or in both directions, or played in other configurations. A trill may be added to the upper note of the next-to-last chord.

CONVENTIONAL ALTERATIONS OF RHYTHM

Along with the freedom to add embellishments, certain freedoms were permitted the performer in the execution of rhythm. This license was not unlike that granted (and even demanded of) the jazz musician of the present day. If notes notated equally could be made to sound more effective by playing them unequally, this was sometimes done. If dotted notes needed to be shortened to produce a more flowing style, or lengthened for a more crisp rhythmic effect, it was not only allowed, but expected, and students learned this as a part of their understanding of *AFFEKTENLEHRE*, or the "Theory of Affects," which was concerned with the proper addition of ornaments, the alterations of rhythms, and the use of other devices to heighten the expressive content of the music.

DOTTED RHYTHMS

Although a dot after a note served to lengthen that note by half its value, as it does today, in practice the amount of time it added was variable.

1. When dotted notes were played in one voice against triplets in another, the value of the dot was often shortened. The following example from C. P. E. Bach's *ESSAY*, III, 27, shows (a) dotted notes "under-dotted," and (b) equally notated notes played unequally; in both cases for accommodation to the triplet rhythm:

This inconsistency in notation is more easily understood when one realizes that the following notation was not yet in use in Bach's day:

A baroque musician, accustomed to adjusting the value of a dot to suit the *Affekt*, would probably have considered this notation of "two-note triplets" not only unnecessary, but rather illogical.

2. When dotted figures were the characteristic rhythm of a piece or section of a piece, and it was intended to sound particularly majestic, mannered, or vigorous, the note was "over-dotted" (the dot lengthened), and the following note played shorter:

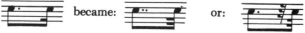

Although the use of the double-dot to convey this rhythm had been suggested by a few composers, it had not yet been adopted as a standard convention of notation.

Many of the dotted notes in J. S. Bach's music are made more effective in performance by over-dotting.

The sharpening of the dotted rhythm is particularly appropriate in *Prelude No. 21 in Bb Major*, beginning in measure 11 and continuing through measure 15 (p. 182).

Such an interpretation of dotted notes is referred to by J. J. Quantz in his *ESSAY*, Ch. XII, 24: "*Majesty [das Prächtige]* is conveyed by dotted notes. These must be enforced with power and attack. The dot is prolonged and the following quickly dispatched." The German *das Prächtige* also refers to things *magnificent*, *sumptuous*, *splendid*, *brilliant*, and *glorious*. This style of playing added to the *AFFEKT* when appropriately applied, and was obviously highly regarded.

3. The manner of playing that has more recently become known as the "French Overture Style" is an extension of the principle of "over-dotting" for grandiose effect. In his *ESSAY*, XVII, vii, 58, Quantz also writes: "When there are three or more 32nd notes after a dot or rest, they are not given their strict value, particularly in slow pieces, but after waiting until the very end of their allotted time, you play them as rapidly as possible. . . and slurring is rarely used."

Further, in Ch. XVII, ii, 16, Quantz remarks: "When 32nd notes follow a long note and a short rest, they must always be played very rapidly, whether in *Adagio* or *Allegro*. Thus, before playing the quick notes, you wait until the very end of the time reserved for them, so as to avoid getting out of time." This style is effective in several of the preludes in this book, most notably *Prelude No. 8 in Eb Minor*, beginning on p. 88.

In his *INTERPRETATION OF THE MUSIC OF THE XVII & XVIII CENTURIES* (London, 1915, new ed. 1946, p. 65) Arnold Dolmetsch cited *Fugue No. 5 in D Major* as an example of the "French Overture Style." He recommended the following interpretation, according to the rules outlined by Quantz and supported by others. Dolmetsch performed it in this fashion in his historic recording on the clavichord, sponsored by 'The 48 Society' of England. (More details concerning this recording are given on p. 217.) Compare the following with the original notation of this fugue on pp. 70-71 of the present volume.

Fugue No. 5 (measures 1-3) as interpreted by Dolmetsch:

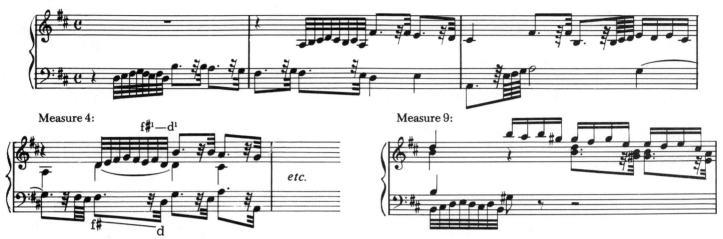

Many performers have been reluctant to accept the above interpretation, but some outstanding artists, including the late Wanda Landowska, have accepted it literally.

Several points are contra-indicative of over-dotting here. In C. P. E. Bach's *ESSAY* Part II (1762) XXIX, 15, we read: "According to the rule, notes which follow dots are played with the greatest rapidity, and this is very often true. But sometimes the notes in other voices, with which such notes coincide, are so divided that the rule must be modified."

In the same *ESSAY*, Part I, iii, 23, the following is given as an example in which "the division must agree with the notated values":

In measure 4, above, the application of over-dotting results in undesirable consecutive octaves: soprano f#¹-d¹ against bass f#-d.

In measure 9 and similar contexts, over-dotting seems even less appropriate. It is the nature of baroque music to synchronize rhythms rather than to force them into disagreement. An important point to consider is the fact that the soprano motive _____ is derived by augmentation of the last four of the opening group of eight 32nd notes. Over-dotting can only weaken the effectiveness of the augmentation.

The rapid dispatch of the three-note groups of 32nd notes, notated in measure 3 of the above example as 64th notes, seems effective and appropriate, and there is no doubt that over-dotting on the fourth count of measure 22 (see p. 73) is advisable. Over-dotting could well be applied to notes that do not conflict with rhythms in other voices, and although this might seem a bit inconsistent, it may be exactly the type of thing C. P. E. Bach is advocating in the quotation cited above. As for the adoption of the Dolmetsch interpretation *en toto*, the rights extended the performer are considerably broad. Each individual must weigh the results and make a personal decision.

NOTES INÉGALES

The convention of playing certain pairs of equally-notated notes unequally, called *notes inégales*, is described and explained by François Couperin in his *L'ART DE TOUCHER LE CLAVECIN* (Paris, 1716, edited and translated by Margery Halford, Alfred Publishing Co., Sherman Oaks, Ca. 1974).

To the French, *notes inégales* made music "more graceful and more pleasant to the ear." The use of this device is also referred to in the writings of early Italian, Spanish, German, and English composers. In his book *INTERPRETATION OF EARLY MUSIC*, ed. of 1973, pp. 462-463, Robert Don-

ington offers evidence that inequality was, on occasion, applied to the music of Handel and J. S. Bach.

Only notes that fall naturally into pairs are eligible for inequality. Notes slurred in groups of three or more are not eligible. But if they are slurred in pairs, that is sometimes an invitation to inequality.

The amount of inequality applied is the performer's option. It may vary from the lilting "long-short," played almost dotted, to the same played almost equal. Sometimes "short-long" inequality is used, even with the first note quickly snapped to the second.

Notes moving conjunctly, slurred in pairs by Bach himself, appear in three selections in this volume. These are *Prelude No. 10 in E Minor*, in the soprano voice in measure 3 (p. 103); *Prelude No. 18 in G♯ Minor*, in the inner voice in measure 7 (p. 156); and in *Fugue No. 24 in B Minor*, in the subject (p. 200). In none of these cases does inequality seem to be demanded. If it is applied to either prelude it must be "short-long," since "long-short" results in a kind of 3 against 2 that seems out of place in this music. It may be applied with some success in No. 10.

In *Fugue No. 24* (p. 200), the slurs introduced in the subject appear later, when these 8th notes are played against 16ths. Since it is the smaller unit to which inequality is applied, it does not seem appropriate here. In the editor's opinion the slurs function to show legato groupings. They seem to indicate written-out appoggiaturas, and are effective when so performed; that is, with the stress on the first note of each pair, resolving more softly to the second.

Inequality should be applied in at least one context in the present volume. When pairs of notes appear in a line of triplets, such as those in the following example from Bach's well-known organ *TOCCATA IN D MINOR*, these paired notes are played unequally, accommodated to the prevailing triplet rhythm. Notice that this applies also to the preliminary note. If this is not done, the passage sounds unnatural.

Organ *TOCCATA IN D MINOR* BWV 565
(measure 4)

This same type of accommodation to the prevailing triplet rhythm must also be applied to the first note of *Prelude No. 6 in D Minor* (p. 74).

Prelude No. 6
(1st measure)

Since inequality was so frequently employed in places where there was no definite indication by the composers, and since performers of the baroque period were allowed so much freedom, it is not impossible that *notes inégales* might be acceptably applied in other selections in this volume. It is conceivable that *Prelude No. 18 in G♯ Minor* might be played in its entirety with "long-short" inequality for the 16th notes. One can also imagine *Prelude No. 4 in C♯ Minor* (p. 56), with "long-short" *inégales* for the 8th notes, and the style would fit well with overdotting the dotted quarters. In his historic recording on the clavichord for the Columbia "Forty-Eight" Society, Arnold Dolmetsch employed *notes inégales* in *Fugue No. 6 in D Minor*, particularly on the 16th notes in the sequence beginning in measure 36 (p. 78). In *Prelude No. 22 in B♭ Minor*, he used them on the 16th notes throughout, and in its companion fugue he used them on the 8th notes. In each case he employed the "long-short" or lilting inequality.

The idea of using *notes inégales* in Bach's music will undoubtedly bring some protests, but many knowledgeable modern performers are doing it. In view of the vast amount of rhythmic freedom allowed the performer in Bach's day, the editor prefers to keep an open mind, to listen, and to experiment.

PHRASING AND ARTICULATION

PHRASING and *ARTICULATION* are not identical commodities. A *PHRASE* (a complete musical thought) needs punctuation, to clearly separate it from the next phrase. Thus it is certainly correct to make a brief "silence of articulation" between one phrase and the next. But *ARTICULATION* means a great deal more than the punctuation of phrase endings. In baroque music in particular, articulation serves to define the shorter motives that make up the structural units within the phrase. This articulation brings such motives into relief, makes the musical content clearer to the listener, and provides stress and emphasis, particularly on those instruments which cannot provide accents, that is, the harpsichord and the organ.

Of the 24 fugues in Volume I of *The Well-Tempered Clavier*, 12 of the subjects begin on the *anacrusis* (upbeat). If we include No. 19, in which

the main part of the subject (after one detached individual note) begins on the anacrusis, this brings the total to more than half. Four more of them begin on the 2nd count of the measure. How important is this for the listener? More than one musicologist has made the statement that, to the ear, the opening of Bach's *Two-Part Invention No. 3* begins on the down-beat, but if Bach's own slurs are observed, this is certainly not true! Here is one case (and a rare one, since Bach has written so few indications for articulation) in which Bach solved the problem for us, and there is much to be learned from this example:

Invention No. 3
(opening measures)

The slurs are Bach's own!

One of the 12 fugues beginning on the anacrusis is *No. 21 in B♭ Major*. Bach indicates no articulation, leaving this, as he generally did, entirely to the performer.

Fugue No. 21
(beginning of subject)
as written by Bach:

If no articulation differences are made on any of these notes, and all are played the same, the opening will sound as follows on the harpsichord or organ (and even on the clavichord or piano unless accents are supplied):

as it sounds without
articulation:

If these notes are slurred in pairs, the undesirable "down-beat effect" becomes more apparent. The Busoni and Czerny interpretations are decidedly unacceptable and only work at all because the pianist can overcome the resulting misplacing of the anacrusis through the use of accentuation of volume:

Busoni Edition: *Czerny Edition:*

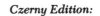

The baroque keyboardist could supply an accent, if he played this on the clavichord, or on the newly invented (but not yet perfected) fortepiano. Yet there is no specific evidence that keyboardists used different articulation on these instruments than on the harpsichord. Pianists can greatly benefit from listening to the subtle and delicate articulation that is necessarily practiced by great harpsichordists. When such stylistic elements are added for musical sense, along with shadings and accentuations of volume appropriate to the *Affekt* of the piece, the result will certainly be more in the true baroque style.

It is not important that *every* beat be clearly defined, not necessarily even the first beat of the measure. The following defines every beat, but is tiresome, and, in several respects, "un-baroque":

Not good:

The entire subject consists of two phrases. The phrases themselves are separated by articulation, but within the phrases there should be additional articulation to clarify the musical substance of the phrases.

Subject in 2 phrases:

In the back of this book, beginning on p. 208, there are tables which show the articulation of each fugue subject, based on various commentaries, editions, and recordings of well-known artists. The tabulations for this fugue are given on p. 215. Special attention is directed to the subtle and effective articulation of Gustav Leonhardt, based on his exemplary recording (Harmonia Mundi 20309-13). Almost every individual beat is defined, without repetitious articulation within the fugue subject:

Leonhardt's phrasing:
(entire subject)

(*very* subtle articulation)

The following articulation is also effective for harpsichord and, if the breaks between the slurs are very subtle, for piano as well.

Also effective:

A different articulation, prepared especially with the piano in mind, is used in our text on pp. 183-185, but any of the above suggestions may be applied, if desired.

The kind of articulation recommended above was typical of baroque practice, even on instruments quite capable of accenting. The folowing example is from J. S. Bach's *CANTATA*, BWV 72, *Alles nur nach Gottes Willen*, No. 4, *Aria*, oboe part. Compare *Fugue No. 3 in C♯ Major*.

BWV 72, 4   *Fugue No. 3*
(1st measure)   (1st measure)

The slurs and staccato   Articulation added
indications are Bach's: by the editor:

When Bach's slurring is properly observed, the ear is not confused. But the articulation must be delicately done. The separations must be almost imperceptible. The rule of the Romantic period, that there must be a very definite lift at the end of the slur, and that the phrasing must taper off in volume near the end of each slur, simply does not apply to this music. Baroque music does not consist of the later hallowed "long legato line."

Slurring across the beat and bar-line is not forbidden, however, as the following example from C. P. E. Bach's *ESSAY*, III, i, 21, illustrates. But this would be completely ineffective unless the pulse of the beat were already established or maintained in the remaining voices.

The basically legato style of playing these preludes and fugues, propagated by Czerny in his edition and followed by numerous later editors, is not according to the general practice of baroque musicians, including J. S. Bach.

The following, from C. P. E. Bach's *ESSAY*, III, 5, is enlightening:

> "The liveliness of the *allegro* is commonly expressed by the use of detached notes, whereas the tenderness of the *adagio* is portrayed in sustained and slurred notes. In performance one must remember that this characteristic and property of the *allegro* and the *adagio* are observed even if it is not indicated in the compositions. . . . I use the expression 'commonly' on purpose, because I realize that all kinds of notes can occur in any tempo."

To this we may add the observation of F. W. Marpurg, a friend and admirer of J. S. Bach, in his *ANLEITUNG*, I, vii:

> "Opposed to legato as well as to staccato is the ordinary movement, which consists of lifting the finger from the last key shortly before touching the next note. This ordinary movement, although it is always understood in absence of other indications, is never indicated."

Since detached playing is such an important element in the performance of this music, the present editor has employed the words *quasi legato* to indicate the use of a very clean touch, almost (but not quite) legato in character. *Quasi non legato* is used to indicate something leaning a bit more toward a detached style, but not excessively. These appear in light gray print, and like all editorial suggestions they may be accepted or disregarded.

Where there is no indication of articulation in the original manuscript, Bach has left the articulation to the discretion of the performer. This is entirely in the baroque spirit of involving the performer in the music along with the composer, very much as we find today in jazz music. Because this is the case, no editor should be allowed to force ideas on the performer. But before the performer makes a decision, familiarity with the style of the period, and a knowledge of what the musicians of that day had in mind, are both extremely important. Since research continues to bring to light information on the correct performance of baroque music, the reader is urged to keep informed, to study, and to listen to authoritative performances. While there are always controversial opinions among experts regarding the ideal articulation for each of these pieces, it is well to bear in mind the fact that there is no *one* correct way to play this music.

DYNAMICS

Since he gave no indications of dynamics whatever in this volume of *The Well-Tempered Clavier*, Bach has once again left the choice to the performer. These pieces were written simply for the clavier (that is, the "keyboard"), and Bach knew that, in his day, they would be performed most frequently on single manual harpsichords and clavichords. This means he was willing for them to be performed with no dynamic changes at all (on a single manual harpsichord) or with very sensitive dynamics (on a clavichord). In his last years, Bach approved of the improved fortepianos built by Silbermann, and it would be difficult to believe that he would not have played these works on those instruments with great enjoyment. Whatever instrument he played, whether a small positive organ or a huge organ with reed stops added to the usual complement of registers, he exploited its possibilities of extreme dynamics and tonal color to the limit. If this music is played on the piano, it should not be limited in dynamic range to the *ppp-mp* available on the clavichord. A fugue does not demand tremendous resources of dynamics to be effective, but it should be allowed to build and subside in a manner that complements the "built in dynamic effects" with which Bach has provided it.

Expressionless playing has no place in baroque music. This is proven by the use of ornaments, as C. P. E. Bach says, "to heighten the expression." Monotony also has no place, and on a two-manual harpsichord provided with registers, it would be sheer nonsense not to make use of its resources to enhance the musical interest of the preludes, and to make the voices of the fugues stand out more clearly.

We do not, on the other hand, advocate an overly romanticized performance, with exaggerated dynamics. We do encourage individualistic interpretation, in keeping with the performer's right to interpret this music, making use of all the freedoms allowed by baroque tradition, as well as all the originality those same traditions demand.

TEMPO

Only a few tempo indications are given by J. S. Bach himself for the pieces contained in this volume. These are found in the present edition in dark print, in *Prelude No. 2 in C Minor, Prelude No. 10 in E Minor,* and in *Prelude and Fugue No. 24 in B Minor.* Once again the composer has given to the performer the freedom of choice that was allowed by baroque tradition, this time with respect to tempo. In making this choice, the performer must bear in mind the expressive nature or *Affekt* of the piece, remembering that long notes, such as those in the subject of *Fugue No. 4 in C♯ Minor,* generally suggest a slower tempo than the small note units of the subject of Fugue No. 7 in E♭ Major.

It should be noted that the effect of slowness is achieved by the length of time-units, and not necessarily by the metronomic beat or pulse. In the first case, above, the time signature is *alla breve,* which in baroque music more often signifies two slow beats than two quick ones.

Kirnberger, among others, has suggested that the choice of a proper tempo for rapid pieces may often depend upon the smallest note values, which must always be heard distinctly.

The metronomic tables in the back of this book, showing the tempo of each prelude and fugue as recommended by various editors and commentators, and as recorded by well-known keyboard artists, should prove helpful. There is agreement here only in the broadest sense, but most of the performances are reasonably convincing. In this area, individual experimentation is recommended, since each performer is allowed to select a tempo in agreement with his or her personal convictions.

Fugue No. 4
(beginning)

Fugue No. 7
(beginning)

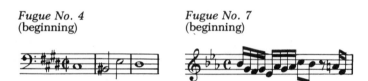

PEDALING

Use of the sustaining pedal, generally speaking, is best avoided in the performance of these preludes and fugues. This is not merely because the keyboard instruments of Bach's day were not equipped with sustaining pedals. Unless the sustaining pedal is used with extreme care, it tends to obscure contrapuntal lines. It is difficult, even in affettuoso passages, to keep the pedal from sounding anachronistic in this music.

It is true that, if it is very judiciously used, the sustaining pedal can occasionally enhance the sound of an arpeggiated chord, without muddling the texture at all. This is especially true in the endings of those preludes that have an improvisatory character, such as Nos. 5 and 6.

The closing measures of *Fugue No. 20 in A Minor* (p. 179) can hardly be performed satisfactorily on

the piano without some assistance from the pedal. This fugue was possibly composed for organ, pedal clavichord, or pedal harpsichord. The long pedal point beginning in measure 85 cannot be executed without the use of a pedal manual or the assistance of a third hand. The sostenuto pedal of a grand piano might be used to make its performance with two hands more practical. The sustaining pedal may be put to use here, according to the editor's suggestions in light print.

The *una corda* ("soft") pedal may be used effectively now and then, for dynamic contrasts such as might be employed in changing manuals on a two-manual harpsichord, especially when a change of tone-color along with a change of volume is desired. The effect should not be overdone.

ABOUT PITCH NOTATION IN THE FOOTNOTES

In order to make the pitch of the notes mentioned in the footnotes perfectly clear and understandable, we have chosen to use a modified version of the Helmholz pitch notation. Helmholtz used C-B, c-b, c'-b', c"-b", c"'-b"'. We use C-B, c-b, c^1-b^1, c^2-b^2, c^3-b^3, as follows:

C-B =   c-b = c^1-b^1 = c^2-b^2 = c^3-b^3 =

The lowest note in The Well-Tempered Clavier is C; the highest, c^3.

PRAELUDIUM 1

ⓐ Andante con moto ♩ = 80-92

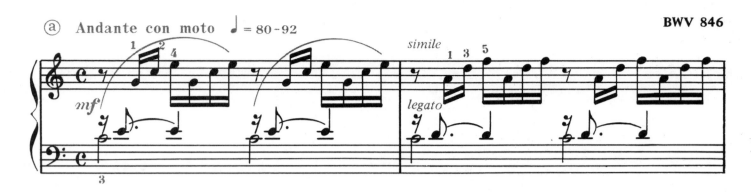

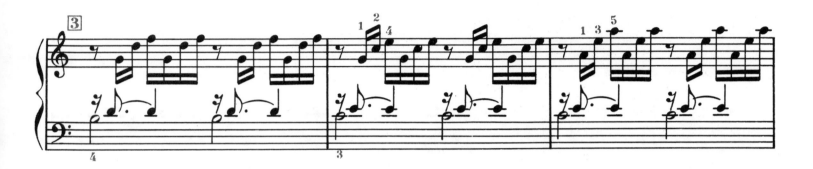

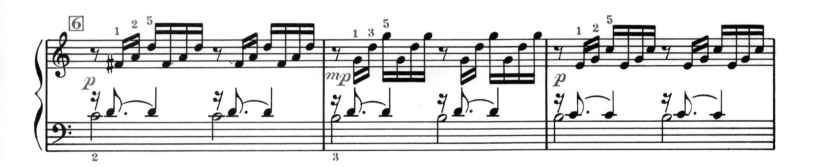

ⓐ Tempo indications in modern editions of the first prelude vary from *Moderato* to *Allegro*. Very few tempo marks appear in Bach's Autographs or in the early sources. All tempo indications in light print are either completely editorial or appear in mss other than the Autographs. A complete table showing tempos taken from various recordings, editions, and commentaries is found on pages 218-219. See also comments in the foreword, on page 17, under *ABOUT THE ARPEGGIATION OF CHORDS*.

ⓑ Beginning here the *Clavier-Büchlein vor Wilhelm Friedemann Bach* has the following.
The broken-chord figurations of the previous measures should be applied here to each
measure except the last.

ⓒ Measures 16-20 are missing in the *Anna Magdalena Notebook* (P225).

ⓓ Between measures 22 and 23 the following measure, originating
as a footnote in the first two Schwencke mss (P203), found its
way into some published editions, including Czerny's. It is not
authentic and should not be played.

(e) The tie in light print is missing from the Autograph and the *Anna Magdalena Notebook* (P225). It is found in the ms of Bach's pupil, H. N. Gerber and in that of Bach's cousin, J. G. Walther (P1074). It is also present in the Fischhof ms (P401). The earlier Schwencke ms (P203) has a whole note C here and in the previous measure.

(f) This trill is found in the earlier Schwencke ms.

(g) The arpeggiando indication is from the Gerber ms. Such chords were customarily arpeggiated, even in the absence of such an indication.

FUGA 1
a 4

FINAL VERSION

NB) On the harpsichord, the following articulation of the subject will help to clarify the position of the beat. The break between the slurs should be almost imperceptible:

Articulation suggested for the harpsichord is also effective on the piano, if the breaks between slurs are made very slight, and if staccato notes are not too short. See the discussion on pp. 24-26.

A table showing phrasing and articulations of the fugue subjects as found in various editions, commentaries, and recordings, begins on page 208.

ⓐ The subject was originally written in the following rhythm:
See the discussion on page 7.

The fugue is presented in its original form beginning on page 36.

ⓑ The reading at the right, from a ms (P205) by an unknown 18th century musician, was adopted in the Tovey edition. Our text is according to Bach's Autograph ms and all of the important sources.

c The reading on the small staff, found in both Schwencke mss and in the Altnikol ms, may be the preferred reading, since the dot was added to the soprano voice at the same time the dot was added to
the alto by an unknown hand.

d Here the Autograph had the following:

This was later changed to avoid consecutive octaves between the tenor and alto voices resulting from
the addition of the dot in the alto. The Tovey edition adopts the following, which stems from the
source mentioned in footnote b :

e Here the Autograph has been altered by an unknown hand, to the point of being almost illegible,
possibly to conform with the readings of Kirnberger and Altnikol shown in the smaller staff. All other
mss consulted are in agreement with our text.

f The trill is found in the Schwencke ms. It is needed at this cadence.

(g) The Kirnberger ms has the following, which was also copied into Bach's Autograph ms (over erasures) by a hand other than Bach's:

(h) Both Schwencke mss have the following rhythm in the soprano voice:

The rhythm is correct when the trill is given its usual realization, as shown in our text in light print.

This trill may also be played as follows: or:

For simplification, a simple turn may be used.

(i) This trill, found in Schwencke P417 does not appear in the Autograph, but is needed at this cadence. See the discussion on page 20.

(j) The c¹ in the tenor voice is a half note in all sources. It is given here as two tied quarter notes, divided between hands, to aid in performance.

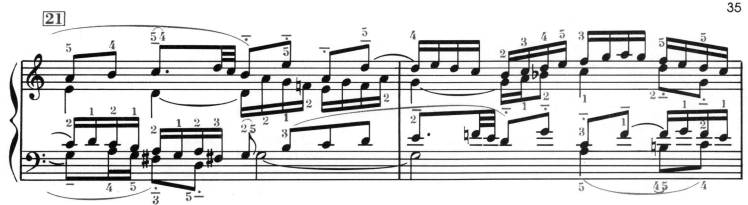

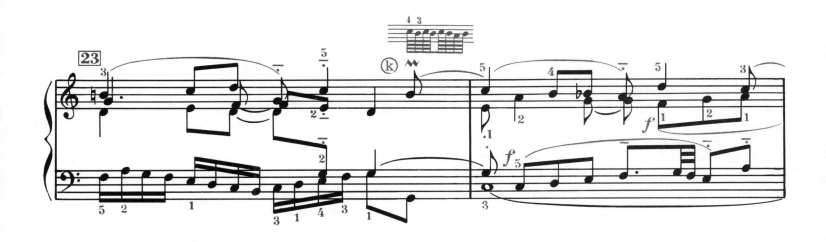

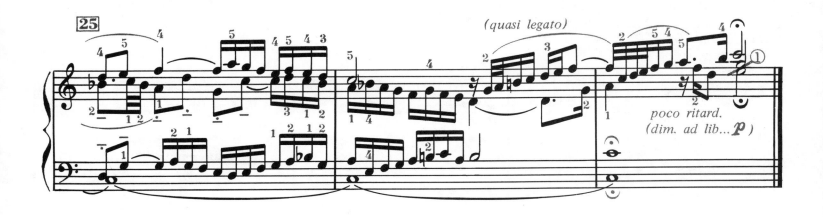

(k) The trill does not appear in any of the early sources consulted but is appropriate at the cadence.

(1) The cross-stroke between e² and g² (a sign for the baroque *acciaccatura*) originates in the Altnikol ms. It is played by breaking the chord from the bottom upwards, adding the dissonant note (f²) at the cross-stroke and releasing it instantly:

FUGA 1
a 4

ORIGINAL VERSION

BWV 846

This is the original form of this fugue, before changes were made in the autograph by an unknown hand. This version is verified in the following mss:

1. The ms of Bach's pupil, H. N. Gerber (1725).
2. The Fischhof ms (P401), an 18th century ms formerly believed to be an autograph.
3. The ms of Bach's cousin, J. G. Walther (P1074).
4. An 18th-century ms (P202), formerly known as the "Second Autograph."

NB) See the bottom of page 32 for comments concerning the articulation of this subject.

ⓐ The trill is found in the Walther ms. The Fischhof ms has what appears to be 〰.

PRAELUDIUM 2

Allegro moderato ♩ = 100–112

ⓐ The *Clavier-Büchlein* has b♭ instead of a♭, here and on the 4th count of the measure.

ⓑ The *Clavier-Büchlein* has g¹ instead of f¹, here and on the 3rd count of the measure.

ⓒ Here the *Clavier-Büchlein* has:

ⓓ The B♭ in our text is according to the Autograph as well as the Kirnberger, Gerber, and Walther mss. Instead of B♭, the two Kroll editions (Peters and Bach-Gesellschaft) have c, which is found in the remaining mss.

ⓔ The word *Adagio* appears in the Gerber ms in what is believed to be Bach's own handwriting.

ⓕ The *d.* and *s.* signs in black print are from the Autograph. Those in light print appear in Schwencke P417 and several other mss. *d.* = *destra* (right hand). *s.* = *sinistra* (left hand).

ⓖ In the *Clavier-Büchlein* this piece ends after measure 26 with the following:

(h) The rhythm here is in accordance with the Autograph and all other primary sources. Only Schwencke P203 has a correct number of counts:

Such use of imprecise rhythmic notation was, according to C. P. E. Bach, often intentional, and served as an indication of *tempo rubato*. (See C. P. E. Bach, *Essay*, I, iii, 28.)

(i) A double mordent may be played here:

A lower appoggiatura & mordent is also appropriate:

(j) Schwencke (P203) has:

(k) The mordent, very effective here, appears in the Gerber ms. A lower appoggiatura & mordent is also appropriate:

FUGA 2

a 3

BWV 847

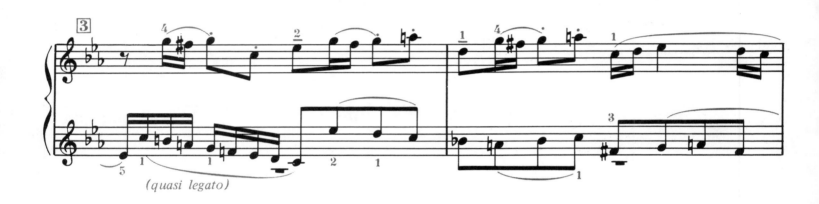

(quasi legato)

cresc.

NB) The suggested articulation of the subject is effective on the piano, and is also acceptable for harpsichord. For harpsichord, however, this can be improved by making an almost imperceptible break before the 2nd and 4th beats of the 1st measure, and before the 2nd beat of the 2nd measure, as follows:

The reason for this is clarified in the discussion on pages 24-26.

The staccato notes should not be extremely short, on piano or harpsichord.
For other possible ways of articulating this subject see the table on pages 208-209.

43

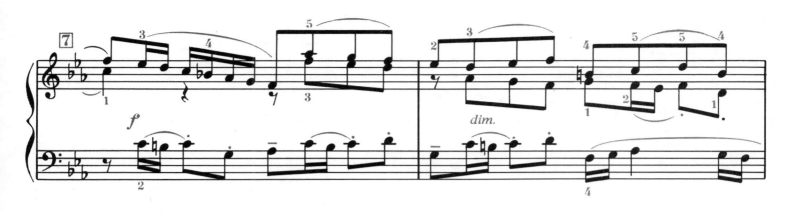

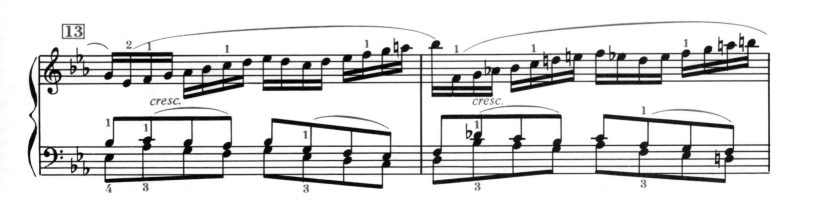

44

ⓐ In the Gerber and Fischhof mss the bass is one octave higher beginning here and continuing
through measure 21. In measure 21 the lower octave (the notes shown in our text) was added in
small notes.

ⓑ Here the Schwencke ms (P203) has:

ⓒ The tie, missing in the Autograph, is present in all other sources.
In his *Essay*, II, iii, 25, C. P. E. Bach states, "The performer should feel free to restrike a long tied note now and then." The upper or lower note of the octave, or both, may be effectively restruck with the final chord, which sounds like a $\frac{6}{4}$ chord if the bass has completely decayed.

ⓓ The fermatas appear in the Kirnberger, Fischhof, Gerber and both Schwencke mss.

PRAELUDIUM 3

Vivace ♩.= 84-92

ⓐ Original version:

BWV 848

ⓐ The notes in the smaller staffs marked "original version" are found in the following mss: The *Clavier-Büchlein vor Wilhelm Friedemann Bach* (in the hand of Wilhelm Friedemann), the Fischhof ms, the 18-century ms numbered P202 (except for measures 17 & 55), the Walther ms, Schwencke (P417) and Forkel mss. These notes were also originally in Bach's Autograph, but they were erased and replaced by the notes in our main text. This latter version is verified in all the other sources consulted. (See the list on pages 5-6.)

ⓑ Here the Forkel ms has:

ⓒ Here the Altnikol ms has:

ⓓ Here the Forkel ms ends as follows. Compare with measures 99-104:

ⓔ P202 and both Schwencke mss have:
The *Clavier-Büchlein* contains the same
variant only in measure 74.

(f) In the Altnikol ms this measure is repeated, as is the following one.

(g) This G♯ and the g♯ in measure 101 are missing from the *Clavier-Büchlein* and the Kirnberger ms.

(h) The chords may be slightly arpeggiated, according to the tradition of the period.

(i) The *Clavier-Büchlein* has: P202 and Schwencke P203 have:

FUGA 3
a 3

BWV 848

NB) This articulation is based on indications J. S. Bach himself used in a similar theme in one of his cantatas, in the oboe part. See the discussion on page 25. This articulation is effective for any keyboard instrument, but the breaks after the slurred 16th notes should be so slight as to be almost imperceptible. Other suggestions for articulation of this fugue subject will be found in the table on page 209.

ⓐ No accidental appears before this f². According to the traditional writing practices of Bach's day, the double sharp in the previous beat would no longer be effective without specific indication here. Such omissions are not unusual, however, and may often be regarded as oversight. The Fischhof and Forkel mss verify the double sharp reading. The alternate reading in the small staff, found in the two Schwencke mss as well as the Kirnberger and Altnikol, may also be attributed to a similar omission, or perhaps they were copied from the Autograph, or one from the other.

ⓑ In the Autograph the small note seems to have been inserted here as an afterthought, perhaps by someone other than J. S. Bach. It is found also in the Kirnberger ms and in Schwencke P417.

alternate reading: ©

© The comments in footnote ⓐ apply here as well, except that the f² double sharp is clearly confirmed only in the Fischhof ms. Use of the double sharp results in a consistent reading each time this counter subject appears: a total of 10 times, of which 8 are perfectly clear, and in which the 2nd, 4th, and 6th notes of the sixteenth-note pattern ⬚⬚⬚⬚⬚⬚ are always the same.

ⓓ The Henle "Urtext" shows the *schleifer* (⨯) at the end of the previous measure. This is an error. The ornament, which appears both in the Autograph and in the Fischhof ms, is clearly placed at measure 13, as shown in our text. Instead of a schleifer here, Kirnberger has ⨯ above the b♮².

52

ⓔ This trill, not in the Autograph, is found in the Forkel ms and in Schwencke P203. It is appropriate at this cadence, and is better played than omitted. See the discussion on page 20.

Many editions, including the Henle "Urtext," show the C♯ as an eighth note.
The Autograph clearly shows a quarter note. The eighth note appears only in the two
Schwencke mss. All of our other sources confirm the reading of the Autograph.

ⓖ The ornament ᴖᴡᴡ appears in Bach's Autograph ms and in Schwencke P417. The Walther ms has no ornament here. Kirnberger has ᴡᴡᴡ. The remaining sources have simply **𝆑𝆒**. The trill need not be measured, but must be played rapidly if consecutive fifths with the L. H. notes are to be avoided. See the discussion on page 19, in which this particular ornament is cited. A termination is not particularly appropriate for this trill, because the trill is followed by a repetition of the principal note.

ⓗ The Kroll editions (Bach-Gesellschaft & Peters) and the Czerny edition have an inexplicable c♯¹ here instead of b♯. The sources have b♯, as given in our text.

PRAELUDIUM 4

FINAL VERSION

This is the FINAL VERSION of this praeludium, according to the later mss and according to Bach's amended Autograph ms. Schwencke P203 has some, but not many, of the ornaments of the final version. The ORIGINAL VERSION is on pp 60-62.

ⓐ In this and similar figures the value of the dotted quarter note may be lengthened and the following note shortened, according to the practice of the period. In the Altnikol ms the *arpeggiando* sign on this chord has a hook at the top, indicating that the chord should be broken downwards, beginning with the top note.

ⓑ The realization of the trill as shown allows the tenor voice, which imitates the soprano of the previous measure, to be heard clearly.

ⓒ The trill in light print in measure 4 and the *appoggiatura* in light print in measure 8 are very possibly intended. The realization of the ornaments will be similar to that of measure 2. If the ornaments in light print are ignored, these measures may be played:

MEASURE 4

MEASURE 8

ⓓ Here Schwencke P203 has b♯¹, adopted by Czerny in his edition, but not found in any of the remaining sources.

ⓔ In Kroll's editions, and in the Wiener "Urtext," the tie joining the two a♯¹'s is missing, although it is present in all the mss which give the final form of this praeludium, including Bach's Autograph.

ⓕ Here the Henle "Urtext" has ∿ . The Autograph clearly shows a *mordent*, as do the Kirnberger, Altnikol, and Schwencke P417 mss. None of our sources has ∿ , which in this context is not as appropriate as ∿.

ⓖ Here a trill with *termination* (turned ending) is also appropriate:

ⓗ The passing tone is found in Schwencke P203 and in the Walther ms. (In the latter, the praeludium is in its original form.) In the Altnikol ms, the passing tone has been added as a small 16th note, written before the following bar line.

59

ⓘ The Altnikol ms has 𝄍 , Schwencke P203 has 〰 , Schwencke P417 has 〰 .

ⓙ An *acciaccatura* is appropriate here, often written with a diagonal line: played:

ⓚ Here a *trill with termination* is appropriate, as in measure 13. See footnote ⓖ , page 57.

ⓛ An *ascending appoggiatura and mordent* would be appropriate here: played:

A *simple mordent* or a *long mordent* on the soprano c♯² are also effective.

PRAELUDIUM 4

ORIGINAL VERSION

Andante espressivo ♩ = 80–92

This unornamented version is found in the *Clavier-Büchlein vor Wilhelm Friedemann Bach*, in the hand of Friedemann himself. It is confirmed in the Walther and Fischhof mss and in P202. The Autograph presumably contained this version before additions were made by an unknown hand. This version is frequently performed, whereas the original versions of the other preludes and fugues which have two forms are seldom heard. This is due to the fact that the Czerny, Busoni, Hughes, and other editions, including Kroll's early editions for Peters, used this version as a basis, whereas in other cases they chose to present the final versions.

ⓐ All chords may be slightly arpeggiated, whether this is indicated or not.

ⓑ Here the Czerny edition has b♯¹, rather than b♮¹. The sharp sign is found only in Schwencke P203. Since it is absent in all the remaining sources including the Autograph, it cannot be considered to be correct.

ⓒ In the *Clavier-Büchlein* and the Fischhof ms the tie joining the two a♯¹'s is missing. Kroll omitted it in both of his editions (Peters & Bach-Gesellschaft) although the B-G edition was based on the final version, all the mss (including Bach's Autograph) clearly contain the tie.

(d) A trill is needed here because of the cadence, or a *turn* may be used as in measure 13 of the FINAL VERSION (see page 57).

(e) The following strange reading found in the Czerny edition, beginning here and continuing through measure 18, has no foundation in the sources. It seems to be Czerny's own arrangement:

(f) The passing tone is from the Walther ms.

(g) For measures 26-27 the Walther ms has:

(h) In the Czerny editions this B is sharped (see the Walther example just above).

(i) A trill or *turn* is needed here, as in measure 34 of the FINAL VERSION (see page 59).

FUGA 4
a 5

BWV 849

(a) The earlier Kroll edition (Peters) erroneously omits the soprano e^2. In the AMSCO reprint of this old version this has been corrected.

(b) In the Altnikol ms there is a tie between the two $c\sharp^1$'s.

(c) In P202 and Schwencke P203 the upper voice has $f\sharp^1$ instead of $g\sharp^1$.

(d) The Kirnberger and Schwencke P417 mss have, for the bass voice, B instead of $c\sharp$.

(e)   In Schwencke P203 and in P202, there is a sharp before this e¹. The Czerny edition has the
e♮¹ as a quarter note followed by a half note, not tied, a reading not found in any of our
sources.

(f)   The whole note is missing in the Altnikol and Walther mss, which have two half notes
(c♯¹). The second half note is tied into the following measure.

(g)   This is the original reading of the Autograph before changes were made. The Fischhof and
Walther mss and P202 have the same.

(h)   Although a♯ seems to be the correct note, the accidental ♯ (necessary according to old
writing practices) does not appear in the Autograph or any of the sources. This seems to be
an oversight. The Kreutz and Wiener "Urtexts" have a natural sign here. The Henle
"Urtext" does not. In the Kirnberger ms there are no accidentals on the a's in this measure.

(i)   The Czerny edition has the upper voice as follows:
This, although obviously conceived as a sequential development of the previous measure,
is by Czerny and not by Bach.

(j)   Here the eighth notes in the soprano seem to constitute, in effect, an ornamented whole
note (f♯²) beginning a statement of the first subject, which continues in the following
measures. Tovey has commented that here the second subject "broadens out into the first."

poco marcato

ⓚ In the Walther ms the f♯¹'s are tied. Walther has similar ties almost every time this motive occurs throughout the fugue.

① From this point, the ms P202 is in the handwriting of Anna Magdalena Bach and thus becomes much more important as a source. This will now be referred to as the ANNA MAGDALENA MANUSCRIPT.

66

(m) In the Czerny edition the alto voice here is given as:
This is not in agreement with any of the sources.

(n) Here Schwencke P203 has:

○ The Autograph, the Anna Magdalena ms (P202), the Walther, Altnikol, Schwencke P417, Fischhof, and Kirnberger mss have a whole note f♯², as shown in our text. Only Schwencke P203 has a half note. The Henle and Wiener "Urtexts" have a half note. The Bischoff and Tovey editions have a half note, "to preserve the five-voice movement."

℗ Here the bass note may be struck again, according to C. P. E. Bach's suggestions regarding long, tied notes in the bass (See footnote ©️ on page 45.)

PRAELUDIUM   5

ⓐ   The *Clavier-Büchlein vor Wilhelm Friedemann Bach* has e¹ instead of c♯¹.

ⓑ   In the Walther ms the c¹ is ♮ .

ⓒ   The *Clavier-Büchlein* has:

(d) In the *Clavier-Büchlein* there are no accidentals in this measure.

(e) The *Clavier-Büchlein* skips from here to measure 27, ending abruptly after one count of measure 27. A shortened version is implied, omitting measures 21-26.

(f) In Schwencke P203 and in the Czerny edition there are ♮ signs before the f² and the f.

(g) In Schwencke P203, P417 and the Kirnberger ms the bass is B instead of A.

(h) The arpeggiation indicated here in the Autograph and other sources implies that the remaining chords should also be broadly arpeggiated. They may be broken upward and downward, if desired, or even broken in elaborate configurations. See the discussion on page 21.

(i) The trill, not in any of the sources, is appropriate at the final cadence.

FUGA 5

a 4

NB) The performance of this fugue with "over-dotting" throughout, suggested by Arnold Dolmetsch, as indicated in the staffs in light print, is controversial. This is a case in which the final decision rests with the convictions and preference of the individual performer. See the discussion on pages 22-23. For suggestions regarding the articulation of the subject, see the table on page 209.

ⓐ In the manuscript of Anna Magdalena Bach (P202), there are alignment lines here and in many subsequent measures, showing that the 16th note following the dotted eighth should be played together with the penultimate 32nd note of the group, as written. Since it is not known when or by whom these lines were added, they do not contribute important evidence that over-dotting should not be used.

ⓑ In the Walther manuscript, in this one instance, the figure ♩. ♫ is written: ♩♫

(c) In the Autograph the b¹ in the R.H. chord has been erased. This may have been done to "correct" the apparent parallel octaves between the alto (b¹-a¹) and the bass (B-A). The stemming makes it clear that the tenor g¹ moves up to the a¹, however. In the Walther ms the voice leading is clarified by two crossing lines:

(d) The use of "over-dotting" against the even sixteenths of another voice, here and in similar situations is especially controversial and is not observed by some artists who do use the exaggerated rhythm in other measures. See the discussion on page 23.

(e) Here the Autograph has something which was construed by Bischoff and Kreutz to be an *appoggiatura*, indicated by apostrophes:

The Henle and Wiener "Urtexts" and Bach-Gesellschaft edition have a small note:

The sign is unclear and may in fact be nothing at all. If it is an *appoggiatura*, it cannot be realized according to the rules (played as an eighth note, it creates consecutive octaves with the d-c♯ in the bass). It does not appear in any other source and is probably best ignored, since the use of such an *appoggiatura* is not in the best context here.

ⓕ The following reading appears only in the Forkel ms:

Hermann Keller has speculated that Bach's ms may have been in error here, since the subject appears nowhere else in the fugue with an octave leap. This, however, is not an entry of the subject, as the intervals that follow the octave in the main text prove. The Forkel version was adopted in the old Hoffmeister edition, and found its way from there into the Czerny edition. Kroll used it in his critical edition for Peters but discarded it in favor of the reading of the Autograph and the remaining sources in his later edition for the Bach-Gesellschaft.

ⓖ The trill, appropriate at the cadence, is found in Schwencke P203.

(h) None of the trills need have the precise number of repercussions shown in the realizations. Here the Kirnberger ms has ⌐ᴡ.
Played, approximately:

(i) The Kirnberger ms has ⌐ᴡ . Played, approximately:
Schwencke P417 has 𝆯 . The meaning is the same as ᴡ .

The exaggerated rhythm is especially appropriate here, both in the treble and the bass.

(j) The trill, although missing in the sources, is appropriate at the final cadence. A turned ending, instead of an anticipation, may be used, if preferred.

PRAELUDIUM 6

Allegro moderato ♩ = 70 - 80
(quasi non legato)

BWV 851

ⓐ The first sixteenth note should be adapted to the prevailing triplet rhythm:

See the discussion of this measure on page 24.

ⓑ In the *Clavier-Büchlein vor Wilhelm Friedemann Bach,* the piece ends here with the following chord:

ⓒ The closing chords may be arpeggiated freely, according to the practice of the period.

ⓓ The Czerny edition omits the b♮¹ in the treble chord.

FUGA 6
a 3

(a) Although the Henle and Kreutz "Urtexts," Bach-Gesellschaft, Bischoff, and some other editions show a wedge-shaped staccato mark here and in several other measures in this fugue, Bach's own staccato indications are clearly intended to be dots. See the proof of this in the discussion on page 7.

(b) The slur, which appears in the Autograph and the Fischoff ms, has been ignored in all other editions except the Wiener "Urtext," which shows it encompassing all four notes of the sixteenth-note group. It may possibly be intended to encompass only the two notes g¹ and f¹. The editor interprets this slur to be an indication that the sixteenth-note groups here and in similar measures are to be played *legato*.

(c) The trills in light print, here and in measure 23, are found in Schwencke P203.

(d) The turns here and in measures 10 and 11 appear in the Autograph but were added later. They do not seem to be in Bach's handwriting. Schwencke P203 has 𝆒 in each of the three places, which seems more appropriate, since it has been established in the subject. If the trill is used, it should be played with the termination or turned ending, as shown in the realization in measure 2, etc. If a turn were used instead it would, in this editor's opinion, merely serve as a simplification of a trill with termination.

(e) Here the Altnikol and Anna Magdalena Bach (P202) mss have *tr* . In any case, ᴍᴍᴡ and *tr* are, in this context, played the same, since the trill is best played with a termination. (See the discussion on **pages 14-15.**)

(f) The Walther and Fischhof mss have: This is thought by some to be an earlier version.

(g) The sharp sign before the c is missing in the Autograph. It is present in the Altnikol ms and in Schwencke P417.

(h) The Czerny edition has the following, which does not originate in any of our sources:

(i) The Henle "Urtext" has a tie joining the upper voice of the final chord to the dotted half note in the previous measure. There is no such tie in the Autograph, in the Anna Magdalena ms, the Walther ms, or Schwencke P203.

PRAELUDIUM 7

BWV 852

This *praeludium* is in itself a short prelude and double fugue. The prelude portion ends with the first count of measure 10. After this cadence, the parts begin to suggest the first fugue subject, which is first heard in its entirety in the bass, beginning with the last quarter note of measure 18. This five-note subject appears again in the bass against the second fugue subject, which enters after the first sixteenth note of measure 25 in the soprano. The legato first subject should be brought out with relative prominence at each appearance.

ⓐ In the Gerber ms the B♭ is repeated on the second count and held for the rest of the measure. It is not tied to the following measure.

ⓑ Here the Walther ms has: The Altnikol ms has:

The half note c² is missing in the Altnikol and Gerber mss.

ⓒ This trill, appropriate at the cadence, is found in the Anna Magdalena Bach ms.

ⓓ **The Walther ms has:** This was adopted by Czerny in his edition.

(e) The trill, found only in Schwencke P203, is appropriate at the cadence.

(f) Here the original version seems preferable, since it is more closely related to the theme.

(g) The flat sign before the d² is missing in the Autograph but is present in the Anna Magdalena Bach ms and all of our other sources except the Altnikol ms.

(h) The trill, found in the Anna Magdalena Bach ms and in Schwencke P203, is appropriate at the cadence.

(i) In the Walther ms and in Schwencke P203 the f is tied to the one on the previous beat. Here the Czerny edition inexplicably omits the f and doubles the bass B♭ an octave higher.

(j) The two b♭'s are tied across the bar line in the Kirnberger, Gerber, Altnikol, and both Schwencke mss.

Ⓚ Here the Czerny edition has a flat sign before the d¹, not found in any of our sources.

Ⓛ In the Anna Magadalena Bach ms and in the Gerber ms these two a¹'s are tied across the bar-line. This reading was adopted by Czerny and by Kroll for his edition for C. F. Peters, but not in his edition for the Bach-Gesellschaft. In Schwencke P203, instead of two eighth notes there is a quarter note, tied. The tie is also accepted in the Henle "Urtext."

Ⓜ Here the Walther ms and Schwencke P203 have:  This reading was adopted in the Czerny edition.

FUGA 7

a 3

In Busoni's edition the E♭ major fugue from volume II of the *Well-Tempered Clavier* was substituted for this one because, Busoni said, "this fugue seems utterly incongruous to the prelude." This presumptuous act is, of course, unwarranted. The prelude is, in itself, a short prelude and double fugue. To follow such a composition with another fugue of similar character rather than a contrasting one would not have been nearly so effective as Bach's own solution, which, needless to say, no editor has a right to change.

ⓐ The trills may be played as follows, to simplify their execution in the more difficult passages such as measures 7, 12, 27, and 35:

ⓑ Beginning here the Fischhof ms has:

ⓒ In the Anna Magdalena Bach ms, and in the Fischhof, Altnikol, and both Schwencke mss, this note is f instead of g. This could possibly have been the original reading in the Autograph before changes were made.

ⓓ Here the Anna Magdalena Bach ms has e♭ instead of f.

(e) In the Walther ms this a is marked natural. Czerny adopted this reading in his edition and has a ♮ also on the next beat.

(f) This trill appears in the Altnikol and both Schwencke mss.

(g) The trill appears in Schwencke P203.

(h) Here the Walther ms has e♭¹ instead of f¹.

PRAELUDIUM 8

BWV 853

The research work sheets for this *praeludium* are reproduced on page 6.

ⓐ The exaggerated rhythms shown in the realizations are in accordance with the performance practices of the period. See the discussion on pages 22 and 23. The trills need not have
precisely the number of repercussions shown in the realizations, which are intended only
to show the general configurations.

ⓑ In Schwencke P203 there is a mordent sign (𝄽) over each of these three notes.

ⓒ Here Schwencke P203 has a mordent instead of a trill. The Anna Magdalena Bach ms
(P202) has 〰〰 .

The arpeggiation signs indicate that the chords should be broadly spread. All other chords
may also be slightly spread.

ⓔ In Schwencke P203 the top note of the chord is $b^{\flat 2}$ instead of $c^{\flat 3}$.

ⓕ In the *Clavier-Büchlein* this chord is the same as the previous one. In the Anna Magdalena
Bach ms, the $e^{\flat 2}$ is missing from the chord.

ⓖ In the *Clavier-Büchlein* this note is $d^{\natural 1}$ instead of $c^{\natural 1}$.

(h) Here Schwencke P417 has a mordent instead of a trill.

(i) The rhythm in the Kirnberger and Altnikol ms is ♩. ♫♫♫
The Anna Magdalena Bach ms has: ♩. ♫♫♫

(j) The *Clavier-Büchlein* has 〰 instead of 〰 . Schwencke P203 has 𝄮 . (〰 and 𝄮 mean the same and were used interchangeably by Bach himself. For 〰 , see page 16, No. 13.)

(k) The Anna Magdalena Bach ms has a small eighth note d♭¹ (appoggiatura) before the c¹. The natural before the c¹ is inadvertently omitted.

(l) In the *Clavier-Büchlein* the ♭ before the f¹ is missing.

(m) Here Schwencke P417 has a mordent instead of a trill. Schwencke P203, the Anna Magdalena Bach and Altnikol mss have 𝄮 .

(n) The slurs in light print here and in the following measure are from the Anna Magdalena Bach ms.

ⓞ The Anna Magdalena Bach ms has:

ⓟ The Altnikol ms has:

ⓠ The trill is found only in the Anna Magdalena Bach ms. It is appropriate at the cadence.

ⓡ The arpeggiation signs in light print here and in the following 4 measures are from the Anna Magdalena Bach ms. The first four signs are found also in Schwencke P203. All but the first 3 are found in the Gerber ms.

(s) Here the *Clavier Büchlein* has b♮¹ instead of g♮¹, presumably an error.

(t) In the *Clavier-Büchlein*, this praeludium is incomplete and ends here.

(u) The sign ↄ, which appears in the Autograph and the Kirnberger ms, indicates a long appoggiatura from above, as shown in the realization in light print. The Anna Magdalena Bach ms has  . This may possibly be confirmed in Schwencke P417, in which

the two curved appoggiatura signs are spaced as follows:

The Altnikol ms has:

In J. S. Bach's Autograph ms, reproduced here in facsimile, the double hook seems to clearly involve only the upper voice. The clef sign for this staff (not shown in the facsimile) places middle (c¹) on the bottom line.

(v) The Anna Magdalena Bach ms has:

FUGA 8
a 3

In most editions this *fugue* is transposed to E♭ minor. We retain the original key, D♯ minor, as it appears in the autograph and all of our sources.

NB) This fugue is traditionally played *legato* throughout. The suggested articulation is effective on all keyboard instruments, but the breaks between slurs must be very inconspicuous. For additional suggestions regarding articulation of this subject, see the table on page 210.

ⓐ Here and in measures 5, 10, & 11, trill signs were added to the Anna Magdalena Bach ms later, and in an unknown hand. Bischoff has termed these trills "of doubtful authenticity." Kreutz refers to them as "superfluous."

ⓑ Here the Autograph and several of the other ms have an obviously erroneous b♮ instead of b♯. Many theorists, including Hermann Keller and Sir Donald Francis Tovey, have assumed, for several logical reasons, that this fugue was transposed from an earlier original in D minor. If so, the b♮ is simply an error in transposition.

(c) The notes of the smaller staff, found only in the Walther ms, represent what J. S. Bach probably intended here, and what he might have written had he not confined himself to the limited range of most clavichords of his day. If his fugue was transposed from D minor, as speculated in the previous footnote, the highest note of the small staff would have been c♮³, thus playable on such instruments in the original key.

(d) Here the Kirnberger, Walther, and Gerber ms have g♯¹ instead of a♯¹.

(e) This trill is found in the Anna Magdalena Bach, Forkel, and Walther ms.

(f) The notes in the small staff marked "original version" here and in measures 41, 52, 73 & 74 are confirmed in the Anna Magdalena Bach, Fischhof, Gerber, Walther, Forkel, & Schwencke P417 ms. The notes in our main text are written over erasures in the Autograph and are confirmed by the Kirnberger, Altnikol, and Schwencke P203 ms.

(g) The natural sign before the e seems to be correct, but is omitted in all our sources.

(h) In the Walther ms there is a trill sign over the bass note, B.

ⓘ In the Walther ms a trill sign appears over the bass note, g♯.

ⓙ In the Walther ms the middle voice is:

(k) The mss containing the original version have no ornament here, except Schwencke P417, which has 〰️. The Kirnberger ms has 〽️ and a small sixteenth note (a♯) before the next bass note, c♯¹.

(l) In the Walther ms and in Schwencke P417 the f𝄪¹ is a quarter note, and there is no a♯ on the next half of the beat.

PRAELUDIUM 9

BWV 854

Andante grazioso ♩.= 60 - 66

ⓐ The trills on eighth notes may also be played:

ⓑ Here the Altnikol ms and the Gerber have a simple trill. Walther has ⩘.

ⓒ In the *Clavier-Büchlein* the bass note is restruck on the 3rd beat.

ⓓ This trill is missing in the *Clavier-Büchlein* and in the Anna Magdalena Bach, Fischhof, Gerber, and Altnikol mss.

ⓔ In the *Clavier-Büchlein* and the Forkel ms (P212) the middle voice is:

(f) The Czerny edition has a sharp before this a². This does not appear in any of our sources.

(g) In the *Clavier-Büchlein* and the Fischhof ms, this tie and the following one are missing. They are present in the Autograph and in all our other sources.

(h) The ⩗ is found in the *Clavier-Büchlein* only.

(i) Here the Altnikol ms has:

(j) In the *Clavier-Büchlein* and the Forkel ms the middle voice is:

(a) The notes in the smaller staff here and in measures 23, 24, 26, & 27 were in the Autograph before erasures and changes were made. They are confirmed by the Anna Magdalena Bach ms, the Fischhof, Gerber, Walther, Forkel mss, and Schwencke P417. Here the Schwencke P203 has:

(b) In the Anna Magdalena Bach ms the fugue subject enters one beat later, with the sixteenth rest and three sixteenth notes missing. This seems to be simply an error.

(c) Here the Anna Magdalena Bach ms has the following for the middle voice:

(d) Here the original version is confirmed not only by the sources listed in footnote (a), but also by Schwencke P203.

(e) Here the original version causes consecutive fifths with the middle voice (g#-f# against d#²-c#²).

(f) The original version is here confirmed by all sources mentioned in footnote (a), except the Gerber ms and Schwencke P303 have:

The Walther ms has: For the middle voice the Anna Magdalena Bach ms has:

(g) In these three places the bass part in the original version (in the small staff) results in consecutive fifths with the soprano voice. In each case, however, there is a perfect fifth and a diminished fifth, considered acceptable.

(h) This tie, quite clear in the Autograph, is missing in the Bischoff edition and Henle "Urtext."

PRAELUDIUM 10

Andante sostenuto ♩ = 52-60

BWV 855

legato e cantabile

(a) All the trills may, of course, be played with more repercussions.

(b) The notes in the smaller staff marked "original version" here and in measures 7, 9, & 11 were in the Autograph before erasures were made. They are confirmed in the Anna Magdalena Bach (P202), Gerber, Walther, and Schwencke P417 ms, and also in the Fischhof ms, except that in measure 5 Fischhof has:

(c) In the Autograph and the Anna Magdalena Bach and Kirnberger mss the sign ⌣ is used for the appoggiatura, as shown in our text. The Fischhof ms has a small eighth note c². No ornament appears here in the remaining sources. The ornament is resolved on the 2nd of the two tied notes, to avoid consecutive octaves with the bass. See the discussion under ABOUT CONSECUTIVES, page 19.

(d) The sixteenth rest is omitted in the Czerny edition, here and in similar measures.

(e) Schwencke P203 and the Gerber ms have e instead of d.

(f) Here Schwencke P203 and the Gerber ms have c² instead of b¹.

(g) Beginning here the Altnikol ms has the following bass sequence:

(h) In the Fischhof ms the g is sharp.

(i) In the Gerber ms the ♯ is missing from the g; also the third soprano note in this measure is e¹ insted of f♯¹.

PRAELUDIUM 10

SHORTER VERSION, FROM THE CLAVIER-BÜCHLEIN VOR WILHELM FRIEDEMANN BACH

BWV 855

This very abbreviated form of *Praeludium 10* was copied into the *Clavier-Büchlein* by Wilhelm Friedemann. This, the earliest known version, predates the so-called original version given in the previous pages. This vividly illustrates Bach's practice of further elaboration of his original ideas. The florid *cantilena* of the later versions is missing in the *Clavier-Büchlein*, where we find only a progression of chords dominated by an ostinato bass pattern. The *Presto* section is absent at the end of this prelude, and the words *Volti Prae* appear, meaning that this prelude was intended to lead directly to the prelude that followed it, which, in the *Clavier-Büchlein*, is the one in E Major, found on page 97 of the present edition.

FUGA 10

a 2

Allegro ♩ = 92–114

BWV 855

ⓐ Here the Gerber and Anna Magdalena Bach mss omit the ♯ before g¹.

ⓑ In the Altnikol and Fischhof mss this g¹ is sharp.

ⓒ In the Gerber ms the ♯ before g is omitted; thus the piece ends in E minor.
Here Bach's slur is intended to indicate the following manner of performance:

PRAELUDIUM 11

NB) The long trills are best played with more repercussions than the realizations show, to avoid consecutive 5ths with the left hand. See the discussion under ABOUT CONSECUTIVES on page 19. The realizations give the general configurations of the trills.

ⓐ In the *Clavier-Büchlein*, this c is an octave higher.

ⓑ ∿ and ∿ are given as in the Autograph. Anna Magdalena, Kirnberger and Schwencke P417 have ∿ throughout. Walther, Gerber, Schwencke P203 and the *Clavier-Büchlein* indicate simple trills. Altnikol has ∿ in the R.H. in mm 3,4,9, & 10, and in the L.H. in 9 & 10, otherwise *tr* is used. On trills of this length, particularly when followed by an ascending 2nd, a termination is added whether indicated or not, according to C. P. E. Bach's ESSAY.

ⓒ Kirnberger and Schwencke P417 have E instead of D.   ⓓ The ♯ before f² is missing in the *Clavier-Büchlein*.

(e) In the *Clavier-Büchlein* & Fischhof ms the f² and f¹ are ♯.

(f) Here the *Clavier-Büchlein* has:

(g) In the *Clavier-Büchlein*, the trilled
note is b♮¹.

(h) The *Clavier-Büchlein*, Kirnberger, Walther, Schwencke P417, and Gerber mss, have no ornament
here. In the Anna Magdalena Bach ms it seems to be ⌣⋀⋀⏐.

(i) Walther and Gerber have no ornament here. The remaining sources have ♯ or ⋀⋀. It is probably best
to play the trill with a prefix, either ⌢⋀ or ⌣⋀ (as shown in our realization).

(j) In the *Clavier-Büchlein* the praeludium ends abruptly here.

FUGA 11

BWV 856

a 3   Allegro non troppo   ♩.= 54-60

(sixteenth notes non legato)

ⓐ In the Gerber ms there is no ornament here or in measures 12, 16, 45, 48, & 55.

ⓑ Schwencke P417 and the Fischhof ms have:

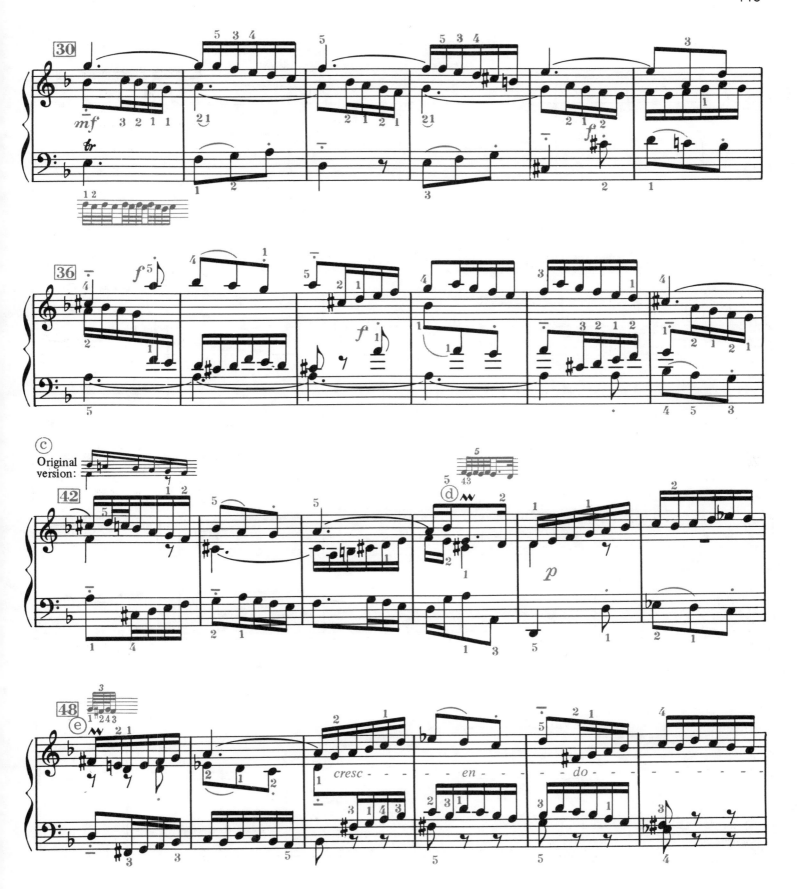

(c) The original version, formerly in the Autograph, is confirmed by the Anna Magdalena Bach, Fischhof, Walther, Gerber, and both Schwencke mss.

(d) Here there is no ornament in the Anna Magdalena Bach, Altnikol, and Gerber mss.

(e) This trill is indicated only in the Autograph.

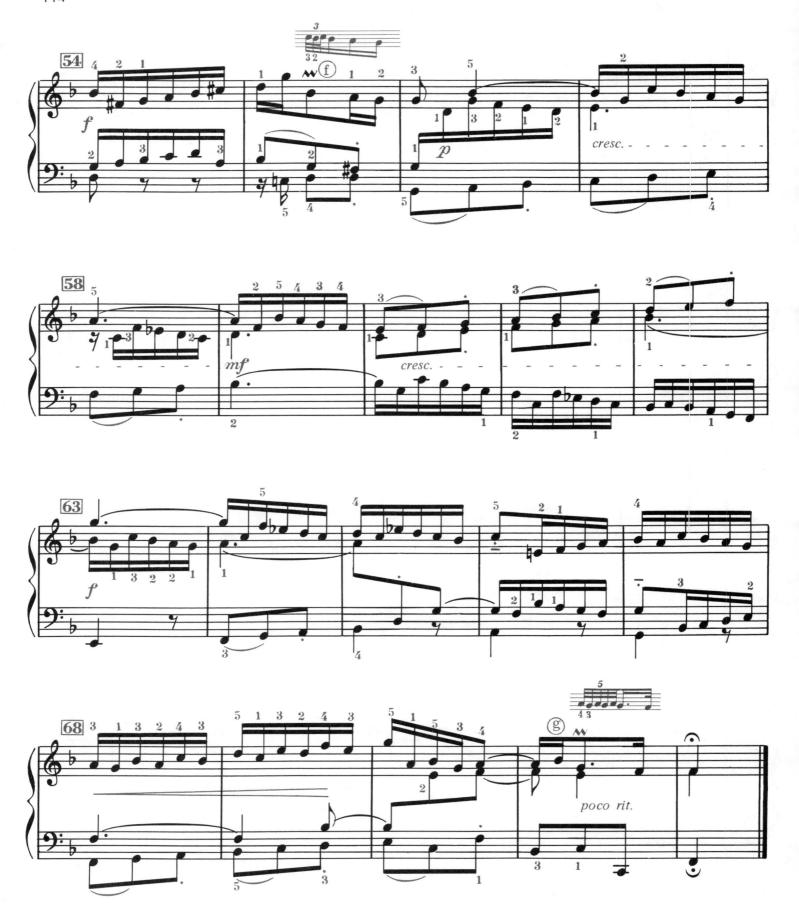

(f) In the Walther ms and in Schwencke P203, the ᷁ᴧ is over the following note.

(g) The trill in light print is found in the Anna Magdalena Bach, Fischhof, and Walther mss and in Schwencke P203. It is appropriate at this cadence.

PRAELUDIUM 12

BWV 857

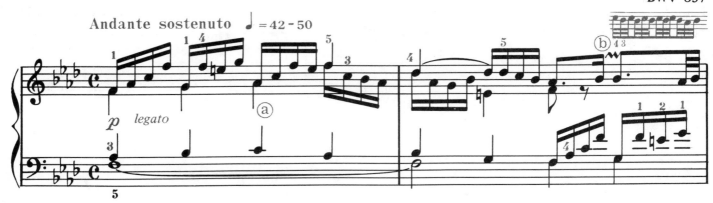

ⓐ In Schwencke P417 the quarter-note stem indicating the alto voice is missing. There are numerous such omissions throughout this praeludium in several of the sources, particularly the two Schwencke mss and the *Clavier-Büchlein*. Since the alto voice is carefully and consistently indicated in the Autograph, these discrepancies, which seem to be simply careless errors, are not itemized.

ⓑ In the Gerber ms there is no ornament here or in measures 3, 4 and 10, or in the left hand in measure 8. The trills need not be measured.

ⓒ In the *Clavier-Büchlein* the ornament is ∿.

ⓓ In the *Clavier-Büchlein* there is no ornament here or in measure 10.

ⓔ In the *Clavier-Büchlein* this and the following three notes of the alto voice are missing.

ⓕ The Anna Magdalena Bach ms has g instead of a♭. All the other sources, including the Autograph, have a♭. The Bach-Gesellschaft edition by Kroll has a♭. The Peters edition by the same editor adopts the g reading; as do Busoni and Hughes. Bischoff prefers the g "because of the sequential construction." The Henle and Wiener "Urtexts" have a♭.

ⓖ In the Anna Magdalena Bach, Altnikol, and Gerber mss, this trill is missing.

ⓗ In the *Clavier-Büchlein* there is a natural sign before this e.

ⓘ In Schwencke P203, the *Clavier-Büchlein*, and the Gerber ms, the trill is missing.

ⓙ In the *Clavier-Büchlein* this c is missing. The tie between the g's in the tenor voice is also missing.

ⓚ In the *Clavier-Büchlein* this c is missing. ⓵ the Altnikol ms has:

ⓜ The original version is confirmed in the *Clavier-Büchlein* and in the Anna Magdalena Bach, Fischhof, Walther, Gerber, and both Schwencke mss. This version was originally in the Autograph but was corrected, apparently by Bach himself, to the reading in our main text.

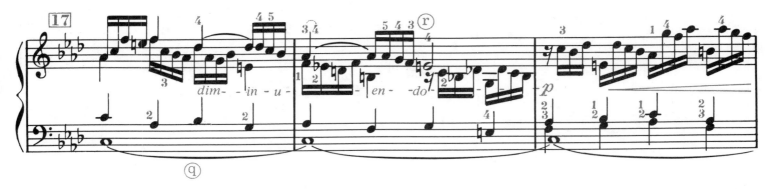

(n)   Here the *Clavier-Büchlein* and the Fischhof ms have:

(o)   Here the Forkel ms ends as follows:

(p)   In the Gerber ms there is a natural sign before this a.

(q)   In the Autograph and the Anna Magdalena Bach ms, this tie is missing. It is present in all the other sources.

(r)   In the *Clavier-Büchlein* this praeludium ends abruptly here.

(s)   The tie in light print is from the Anna Magdalena Bach ms.

(t)   In the Gerber ms there is no natural before the a in the final chord. Thus the prelude ends on a minor, instead of a major chord.

FUGA 12

a 4   Molto moderato, serioso ♩ = 48–56

BWV 857

NB) The breaks between slurs should be practically imperceptible. See the discussion on pages 24–26. The table on page 212 will suggest other possibilities for articulation. On the harpsichord, the following articulation of the countersubject will help to define the beat. The breaks between the slurs should be minimized, as usual:

ⓐ   The trill appears in Schwencke P203 and in the Anna Magdalena Bach ms. It may be omitted.

ⓑ   The ♮ sign before this D appears only in the Fischhof and Walther ms. It is certainly correct.

ⓒ   This trill and the one in measure 9 are from the Anna Magdalena Bach ms. Both may be omitted.

(d)   This d♭ appears as an eighth note in the Autograph and in Schwencke P417, the Walther, Gerber, and Kirnberger mss. Most modern editions have the note as a quarter note, as it is found in the Anna Magdalena Bach ms, Schwencke P203, the Fischhof and Altnikol mss. This seems correct, since in all the other numerous places in which this countersubject appears the note NEVER appears as an eighth note.

(e)   This e♭² is missing from the Walther and Anna Magdalena Bach mss, and the previous note (f²) is a quarter note.

(f)   The trill in light print is from the Anna Magdalena Bach ms. It may be omitted.

(g)   The trill is from the Anna Magdalena Bach ms. It may be omitted.

(h)   The ♮ is missing here in the Anna Magdalena ms.

(i)   The Anna Magdalena Bach ms has:

ⓙ The Altnikol ms has:

(k)   In Schwencke P417 and the Anna Magdalena Bach ms the ♮ is missing before the B.

(l)   The bass note, F, is doubled one octave higher in the Altnikol ms.

PRAELUDIUM 13

Allegretto ♪.=72-88

BWV 858

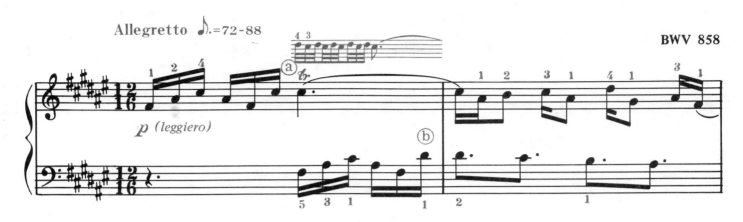

(a) The trill appears in the Fischhof, Walther, Gerber and Anna Magdalena Bach mss. This trill (and the other trills in this prelude) need not be measured. It is effective to prolong the starting note slightly. The trill may be continued longer, even to the first note of the following measure, if desired, although the editor considers the suggested manner of performance to be particularly effective.

(b) In Schwencke P417 and the Walther ms this note is $c\sharp^1$ instead of $d\sharp^1$.

(c) The tie, missing in the Autograph, appears in Schwencke P417 and the Anna Magdalena Bach ms; in Schwencke P203 the two $c\sharp^2$'s are expressed as a single eighth note.

(d) Here the Autograph has 𝆮, as our text shows. The Henle "Urtext" has 〰.

(e) In the Walther ms these two f♯¹'s are tied.

(f) The tie shown in light print appears in the Anna Magdalena Bach ms. In Schwencke P203 the two a♯¹'s are written as a single eighth note.

(g) The trill appears in Schwencke P203 and in the Altnikol and Gerber ms.

(h) The tie appears in the Anna Magdalena Bach ms. Schwencke P203 has a single eighth note g♯¹ here.

ⓘ   The Anna Magdalena Bach ms has: Schwencke P417 has:

ⓙ   The note is a♯¹ instead of g♯¹ in the Kirnberger and both Schwencke mss.

ⓚ   The tie appears in Schwencke P417. There appears to be a tie also in the Kirnberger ms. Schwencke P203 has a single eighth note.

FUGA 13

a 3

Andante con moto ♪=56-60

BWV 858

This entire fugue is missing from the Autograph. The ms of Anna Magdalena Bach (P202) has been used as the principal source for our text.

NB) This suggested articulation is effective on any keyboard instrument. The staccato notes should not be too short, and the breaks between slurs must be very slight. For additional suggestions regarding the articulation of this subject, see the table on page 212.

ⓐ Schwencke P203 has: This reading is logical, since this part of the subject is so played at the beginning.

ⓑ The trill appears in the Fischhof ms and in Schwencke P203.

ⓒ The trill appears in Altnikol, Fischhof, Kirnberger, and both Schwencke mss.

ⓓ Schwencke P203 has: The Czerny edition has:
This is derived from the
old Hoffmeister edition.

ⓔ The trill is missing from the Gerber and Walther mss. In Schwencke P203 it appears over
the following note (e$\sharp^2$), as shown in footnote ⓓ.

ⓕ The trill appears in Schwencke P203 and the Fischhof ms.

PRAELUDIUM 14

ⓐ The first 6 measures, plus the first 3 beats of the 7th, are missing from the Autograph. This poses no particular problem, since all the sources are in substantial agreement on the text of the missing portion.

ⓑ Here Schwencke P417 and the Walther ms have a^1 instead of $g\sharp^1$.

ⓒ Here the Altnikol ms has:

ⓓ The Autograph begins here.

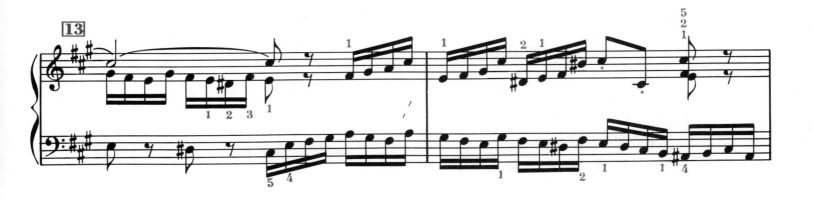

(e) Here our main text is according to the Autograph. Also in agreement are the Gerber, Kirnberger, Walther, Fischhof, and Anna Magdalena Bach mss, and Schwencke P417. Only the Kreutz and the Wiener "Urtexts" have notated this correctly. The reading on the small staff, found only in the Altnikol ms and in Schwencke P203, has been adopted by the Bach-Gesellschaft, Tovey, Bischoff, Czerny, Busoni, and Mason editions, and even the Henle "Urtext."

(f) This trill appears in the Autograph but may have been added later. It is found also in the Kirnberger, Walther, and both Schwencke mss, as well as the Anna Magdalena Bach ms, where it is written ⋏⋏. The Wiener "Urtext" interprets the sign in the Autograph as ⋏⋏, which is a possibility (since the "t" in the trill sign is not crossed, it has that approximate appearance). The trill would sound well in this context with the first note prolonged, as the sign ⋏⋏ would indicate.

(g) This trill appears in the Autograph but seems to be a later addition. It is found in Schwencke P203 and in the Walther and the Anna Magdalena Bach mss, in each case written 𝕎 .

(h) This trill, not in the Autograph, is required at the cadence. It is present in the Altnikol and Walther mss; it appears also in the Anna Magdalena Bach ms and in Schwencke P203, written 𝕎 .

(i) Here the Anna Magdalena Bach ms has e¹ instead of f♯¹.

(j) The Gerber ms has no ♯ before the a, thus the prelude ends with an F♯ minor chord.

FUGA 14
a 4

NB) This fugue subject is traditionally played *legato* throughout. On the harpsichord it will benefit from the following very subtle articulation if the infinitesimal breaks between the slurs are almost unnoticeable:

See the discussion on pages 24-26. For additional suggestions regarding the articulation of this subject, see the table on page 212.

(a) This trill appears in the Anna Magdalena Bach ms, also in Schwencke P203, written *tr*. The presence of the trill in the subject (measure 3) implies that this trill and those in measures 10, 17, 27, and 31 are intended, whether specifically indicated or not.

(b) This trill appears in the Anna Magdalena Bach ms; also in Schwencke P203 and the Walther mss, written *tr*.

© The Gerber ms has:

ⓓ If a trill is added at this cadence, it should have more repercussions than the previous ones, because of the ritard. Because of the importance of the inner voices, the omission of such a trill is acceptable.

ⓔ The ♯ before a is erroneously missing in the Autograph, the Anna Magdalena Bach ms, and the Kirnberger ms (Am B57). In the Gerber ms, this sharp as well as the one before the previous a is missing, and the fugue thus ends with an F♯ minor chord.

136

PRAELUDIUM 15

Allegro ♩ = 70 - 80
(quasi legato)

BWV 860

ⓐ Here and in the following group of sixteenth notes, the Gerber ms has e¹ instead of f#¹.

ⓑ Here the Czerny edition has f♮¹ instead of e¹, derived from the old Hoffmeister edition.

© In Schwencke P203, each of these eighth notes is tied to the following sixteenth.

ⓓ A shorter version, given by Forkel, ends here with the following three measures:

ⓔ In the Gerber ms and in Schwencke P203, there is a sharp before this g.

FUGA 15
a 3

BWV 860

In his edition, Busoni exchanged the G Major fugue of Volume II of the Well-Tempered Clavier with this one.

NB)   For the harpsichord, the following, very subtly articulated, will help to clarify the position of the beat within the phrase.

See the discussion on pages 24-26. For additional suggestions regarding the articulation of this subject, see the table on page 212.

ⓐ In the Anna Magdalena, Gerber, Walther, Altnikol, and Schwencke mss, this d¹ is tied to the following one. The tie is missing in the remaining sources, including Bach's Autograph. The tie was adopted in the Bach-Gesellschaft edition (Kroll), in Kroll's earlier edition for C. F. Peters, and in the Czerny edition. It was not accepted in the Kreutz "Urtext," the Henle "Urtext," the Wiener "Urtext", nor in the Bischoff, Hughes, and Tovey editions. The entrance of the subject in inversion, which begins on the 2nd of the two d¹'s, stands out much more clearly without the tie.

ⓑ The trills need not be measured. They may have additional repercussions, depending on the tempo.

ⓒ This natural sign appears in all of our sources except the Altnikol ms. Some old editions omitted it.

ⓓ This trill and the one in the following measure appear in the Autograph, as well as all of our other sources. In the similar measures 29 & 30, 44 & 45, and 71 & 72, they have been added in light print by the editor. See the discussion on page 20.

140

ⓔ In the Fischhof ms there are natural signs before the first two f♯²'s in this measure. These
signs are also found in some of the older printed editions.

ⓕ The Anna Magdalena Bach ms has the soprano voice as follows:

(g) The trill may continue for the entire measure. Sixty-fourth notes may be used instead of 32nd notes, here and in other trills in this fugue, depending on the tempo.

(h) In the Anna Magdalena Bach, Fischhof, Walther, Altnikol, Gerber, and Schwencke P203 mss the c² and both c's in this measure are sharp; possibly an earlier version. Our text is according to J. S. Bach's Autograph and the remaining sources, and agrees with the two Kroll editions (Bach-Gesellschaft and C. F. Peters) as well as the Kreutz, Henle, and Wiener "Urtexts."

(i) In the mss listed in footnote (h), the alto voice is as follows:

(j) In Schwencke P203 the last three bass notes of this measure are written an octave higher.

PRAELUDIUM 16

BWV 861

(a) Although some prefer to begin this trill on the principal note, there is no historical evidence that such trills were intended to be so performed. This trill need not be measured, but may be played freely. The trills in measures 3, 7, and 11 are similarly played. A termination (turned ending) may not be used, since in measures 7 and 11 the closing notes would produce consecutive octaves with the upper voice. The trill may end on the last quarter, eighth, or sixteenth, or proceed for the entire measure, as desired.

(b) In the Anna Magdalena Bach ms the bass note F is an eighth note instead of a quarter.

(c) The Altnikol ms has: (d) The Gerber ms has:

(e) The Anna Magdalena Bach ms has e♭ instead of d.

(f) In the Walther and Altnikol mss the alto voice is:

The Anna Magdalena Bach ms has: (sic!) The Gerber ms has:

(g) In the Anna Magdalena Bach ms these three notes are erroneously written a third higher.

(h) In the Kirnberger and Gerber mss this is a quarter note, b♭. The following b♮ is missing.

(i) This G appears in all the sources as a whole note. Since it was necessary to divide this measure between two systems, we have used two tied half notes.

(j) In the Gerber ms., the ♮ before b is missing, thus the final chord is G minor.

FUGA 16
a 4

NB) On the harpsichord, the 2nd measure of the subject might be more effectively articulated in one of the following ways:

or

Such slurring suggests a special relationship between the 2nd measure and the 1st. This articulation is also effective on the piano if the breaks between the slurs in the first example are not too obvious, or if the staccato notes in the second example are not too short. For other suggestions regarding the articulation of this fugue subject, see the table on page 213.

ⓐ A trill with *termination* (turned ending) may be appropriately added here, played approximately:

ⓑ Here several old editions have e♮¹, which is found only in the Altnikol ms.

ⓒ   In the Walther ms the bass voice is as follows:

ⓓ   The Czerny edition has no natural before the b, thus ending with a minor chord. The same is true of the Gerber ms. In the Anna Magdalena Bach ms, the natural has been scratched out. The other sources have b♮.

PRAELUDIUM 17

ⓐ In Schwencke P203 the two e♭²'s are tied, as are the corresponding d²'s in the soprano voice ending measure 7 and beginning measure 8.

ⓑ The trill is found in the Anna Magdalena Bach ms, the Gerber, and Schwencke P203.

ⓒ The Walther ms has: 𝄢 ♭♭♭♭ ♩♩♩♩ *etc.*

ⓓ The Walther ms has: 𝄢 ♭♭♭ ♩♩♩♩♩

ⓔ The quarter note down-stem is found only in the Altnikol and Walther mss. It is accepted in all the so-called "Urtexts" without comment.

ⓕ This note is b♭ instead of a♭ in both Schwencke mss and in the Kirnberger and Gerber mss.

ⓖ A trill at the cadence is appropriate, played:

or:

See the discussion on page 20.

FUGA 17

a 4

NB) The indicated articulation of the subject is acceptable on all keyboard instruments. The following is also especially effective:

For additional suggestions, see the table on page 213.

ⓐ This ab² is tied to the previous one in the Altnikol, Walther, and Gerber mss, and in Schwencke P203. The tie was adopted in the Czerny edition.

ⓑ **Schwencke P203 has:**
This was adopted in
the Czerny edition.

Schwencke P417 has:

ⓒ **Schwencke P203 has the bass voice as follows:**

ⓓ **Here the Gerber ms has:** *etc.*

ⓔ In Schwencke P203 the soprano voice is:

In the Altnikol ms, the rhythm
is the same, but ties are used:

(f) In the Altnikol, Gerber, and Schwencke P203 mss the eb²'s and f²'s are tied, as follows:

(g) The ab² is a quarter note in the Anna Magdalena Bach ms.

PRAELUDIUM 18

NB) The traditional *legato* performance of this praeludium is more effective on the piano or clavichord than on the harpsichord. Some harpsichordists use a *"quasi-legato"* throughout, with almost imperceptible breaks at the bar-lines and, in some instances, before the 4th beat of each measure. Others prefer the following:

(a) The alto d² is missing in the Anna Magdalena Bach ms.

(b) The ties here and in measure 11 are clear in the Autograph. Nevertheless, the Henle "Urtext" has them in parentheses.

(c) The slurs are in the Autograph and in all the other sources except Gerber and Walther.

(d) The sharp sign in light print is missing in the Autograph but is present in the Anna Magdalena Bach ms and in most of the other sources. It is undoubtedly correct.

(e) In the Anna Magdalena Bach ms the group of six sixteenth notes ends with an erroneous A♯.

(f)   The Czerny edition has an erroneous double sharp sign before the f♯¹ in the soprano voice.

(g)   The Czerny edition has, erroneously, two eighth notes on g♯¹ instead of one quarter note.

(h)   This tie is missing in Schwencke P417 and in the Kirnberger and Gerber mss.

(i)   In the Gerber ms. there is no sharp sign before the b. In the Anna Magdalena Bach ms the b is marked ♮ in a different handwriting.

FUGA 18

a 4

BWV 863

NB) On the harpsichord, the 4th beat of the first measure may be better defined if there is an almost imperceptible lift before the b. That this seems more important to some harpsichordists than to others is evident from the table on page 213, where additional suggestions for the articulation of this subject will be found.

ⓐ The Gerber ms has the following: There are many small discrepancies in this ms of the fugue, most of which are not worthy of mention.

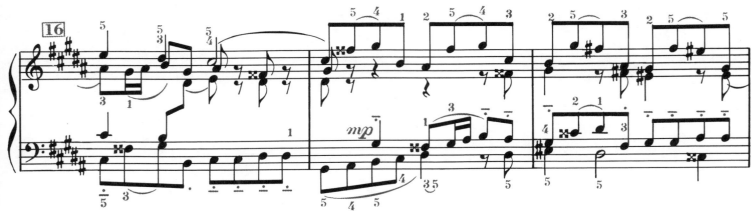

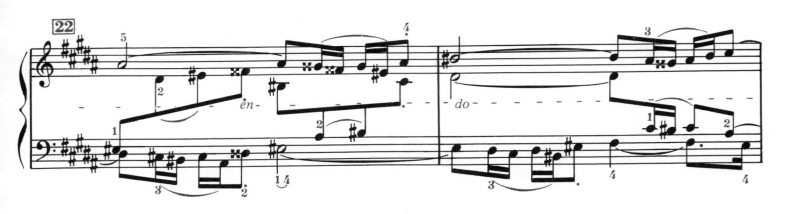

(b) The Altnikol ms has the following:
Schwencke P203 has the same, except the
down-stem is missing from the L.H. g♯.

(c) The sharp before this b is missing in the Anna Magdalena Bach ms. On this evidence, the
Kroll edition (C. F. Peters) gives b♮ as an alternate reading.

(d) The d's in the tenor voice are tied in the Fischhof and Schwencke P203 mss.

(e) The Fischhof, Altnikol, Kirnberger, and both Schwencke mss have a sharp before this b, as do the Henle and Wiener "Urtexts." The Anna Magdalena Bach ms has a natural sign. In the Autograph the sign seems to be a sharp but is rather illegible. All other sources consulted leave the b unsharped, as do the Czerny, Tovey, and Kroll editions. The Kreutz, Bischoff, Hughes, and Bach-Gesellschaft editions have b♮.

PRAELUDIUM 19

BWV 864

Beginning with this Praeludium, the Gerber ms is no longer in Gerber's handwriting. There are many discrepancies, only the most important of which will be noted, since most of them seem to be due to careless copying.

ⓐ Or:  or see the realization of the trill in measure 14.

ⓑ in Czerny's version, but not in any of our sources.

(c) For the middle voice the Czerny edition has ♩♪ This is not found in any of our sources.

(d) The trill is found in the Walther, Altnikol, and Schwencke P203 mss.

(e) The very logical tie in light print is found in both Schwencke mss. In the Walther ms both of the upper voices are tied here.

(f) The Czerny edition has ♩♫ While this is consistent with Czerny's reading of measure 4 (see footnote b), it is not in agreement with Bach's Autograph or any of our sources.

FUGA 19
a 3

NB) *Staccato* applies only to the ordinary eighth notes. Quarter notes (including tied eighth notes) or longer ones should be held for full value. For other possibilities for articulating this subject see the table on page 214.

ⓐ Here the Forkel ms has: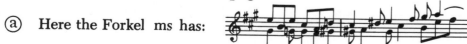

In this ms there are many discrepancies which were itemized in the Bischoff edition solely because they had been adopted in several old editions no longer in print. They can no longer be considered important.

ⓑ In the Walther ms the bass e is doubled an octave higher.

ⓒ Here the Czerny edition has (incorrectly):

ⓓ Here the Czerny edition has the following erroneous reading:

ⓔ Here Schwencke P417 has:
This ms has many small
discrepancies too insig-
nificant to mention.

The Walther and
Forkel mss have:

(f) Instead of the note b¹ the Czerny edition has an erroneous a¹.

(g) Philipp Spitta, Hermann Keller, and others have observed that Bach probably would have written the notes shown here in light print, had he not confined the range of these pieces to the compass of the smaller keyboard instruments of his day.

(h) Here the Anna Magdalena Bach ms has d♯² instead of d♮².

(i) This trill, appropriate at the cadence, is found in the Walther, Forkel, and both Schwencke mss.

ⓙ The trill is found in the Anna Magdalena Bach ms.

ⓚ Here the Anna Magdalena Bach and both Schwencke mss have f♯¹ instead of e¹.

ⓛ Instead of g, the Kirnberger ms has e, a third lower. This is accepted in the Kroll (Peters) edition and given as an alternate reading in the Bach-Gesellschaft edition.

ⓜ Here the Kroll and Busoni editions accept the version found in the Anna Magdalena Bach ms:

ⓝ The trill, though not found in any of the sources, is appropriate at the cadence.

PRAELUDIUM 20

BWV 865

NB) The editor suggests that all eighth notes be played *staccato*, and all sixteenth notes *quasi legato*. Longer notes may be sustained for their full values.

ⓐ Beginning here the Czerny edition has:

This reading is not found in any of our sources.

ⓑ Schwencke P203 has: (sic!)

ⓒ In the Anna Magdalena Bach ms the bass C is a dotted quarter note.

ⓓ In the two Schwencke mss the soprano a² is a dotted quarter note. The Altnikol and Gerber mss have a quarter note with no rest.

(e) In the two Schwencke mss. the soprano e² is a dotted quarter note.

(f) This tie is present in the Fischhof, Altnikol, Gerber, and Schwencke P203 mss. The note may be struck again anyway, according to C. P. E. Bach. In his ESSAY, II, iii, 25, he states, "The performer should feel free to restrike a long tied note now and then."

(g) Some of the mss show different versions of the final chord:

FUGA 20
a 4

BWV 865

Moderato ♩ = 63-72

(non troppo staccato)

NB) On the harpsichord, the following articulation will better define the beat:

Additional suggestions for articulating this subject will be found on page 214.

ⓐ In the Fischhof, Walther, Altnikol, and Schwencke P203 mss, there is a sharp sign before the bass note d.

(b) The Anna Magdalena Bach and Gerber mss have:

(c) Instead of e, the Anna Magdalena Bach ms has g, a third higher.

(d) The trill, needed at the cadence, appears in Schwencke P203.

(e) The Schwencke P417 and Gerber mss have:

This is inconsistent with the rhythm of the inverted subject.

(f) This trill, needed at the cadence, appears in the Anna Magdalena Bach ms.

(g) The Anna Magdalena Bach ms has:

(h) The trill, found in Schwencke P203 and the Anna Magdalena Bach ms, is effective at this cadence.

① Here the Czerny edition has notated (incorrectly):

(j) It is difficult to determine in the Autograph whether this trill and the one in the treble of the next measure are written *tr* or 〰.

(k) This trill sign, missing from the Autograph, is found in Schwencke P203 and in the Anna Magdalena Bach and Altnikol mss.

(l) The trill sign, missing from the Autograph, is found in the Anna Magdalena Bach, the Kirnberger, and both Schwencke mss.

(m) In the Czerny edition there is an incorrect sharp sign before the bass note g.

(n) The Anna Magdalena Bach ms has:

(o) Here, instead of three notes in the alto voice, the Anna Magdalena Bach ms has a quarter note e².

(p) This trill, needed at the cadence, is found in the Anna Magdalena Bach, Altnikol, Walther and Schwencke P203 mss. In the Walther ms, the trill has a termination (32nd notes, d² and e²), instead of the anticipation.

(q) In P202, Anna Magdalena Bach's handwriting ends here. From this point the ms. was completed by J. F. Agricola, a German keyboardist and composer who studied with Johann Sebastian Bach for three years.

(r) The trill, effective at this cadence, is found in the Walther and Agricola (P202) mss. It may be played: [musical example] or as in measure 64.

(s) This g may be taken with the R.H. thumb. The tied note in the soprano voice must be released and re-played on the following beat. The keys of some harpsichords and clavichords are small enough to allow this g to be played with the L.H. thumb, as Bach possibly intended.

ⓣ Here the Henle "urtext" has , possibly derived from the readings of Schwencke P203 and Walther. Our text is in agreement with the Autograph and all the remaining sources consulted.

ⓤ Because it is impossible, using only two hands, to sustain this pedal point "A" to the end of the piece, it has been speculated that this fugue was composed for an instrument with a pedal keyboard, such as the organ, the pedal harpsichord, or the pedal clavichord, or any one of these that might be available to the performer. It is possible to perform these measures on an instrument without a pedal keyboard with reasonable success by restriking the bass note at the beginning of each measure and again on the last half note of the piece. This was acceptable, according to the usual baroque performance practices regarding long, sustained notes. (See footnote ⓒ on page 45.) The last line of music above, in light print, provides an editorial suggestion for performance of these measures on the piano. On instruments equipped with a sostenuto pedal, more effective solutions will be simple to discover.

PRAELUDIUM 21

(a) In the Forkel ms this b♭ is an octave lower. This and several other discrepancies in the Forkel version found their way into the Czerny edition.

(b) The fingering numbers in italics are from the Kirnberger ms. Schwencke P417 also has some fingering numbers which are generally in agreement with Kirnberger. The italic numbers below the notes are for left hand, and those above for right hand.

 Here the Forkel ms and the Czerny edition have:

(d) The word *Adagio* appears in the Fischhof ms. It is recommended that the first chord of this and the following similar groups be arpeggiated and over-dotted (♩.. 𝅘𝅥𝅯𝅘𝅥), according to the practice of the period (see the discussion on page 22).

(e) Here the Henle "Urtext" includes b♭¹ in the first chord as well as the second. This reading is not in agreement with the Autograph.

(f) The eighth-note upstem is missing in the Fischhof, Agricola, and Gerber mss. In the Forkel ms and the Czerny edition, the following b♭¹ is also sustained, with a sixteenth-note upstem.

(g) In the Forkel ms and the Czerny edition, the e♭ is omitted from this chord.

(h) Here a long mordent may be used:
The sign ⁓⁓⁓ , given in
the Henle "Urtext," is not according to the Autograph or any of our sources.

(i) The Czerny edition adds the following measure, called by Tovey "perhaps the most Philistine single printed chord in the whole history of music":

a 3

BWV 866

NB) The articulation suggested in our text is effective for piano, clavichord, or harpsichord. On the harpsichord, however, the following articulation will better define the 2nd beat of the subject, thus making it a bit easier for the listener to follow. See the discussion on pages 24-26.

For additional suggestions, see the table on page 215. On page 25 in the foreword this fugue subject is discussed in detail. The dot above the 2nd sixteenth in measure four will serve to indicate a brief "silence of articulation," which may be used to separate this note a bit from the following one, if desired.

(a) In the Fischhof and Forkel mss the e² and the e in this measure are natural.

(b) In the Forkel ms and in the Czerny edition the flat sign before the a¹ is missing.

(c) For the two upper voices the Forkel ms, possibly for the purpose of simplification, has:

(d) Here the Gerber ms has:

A trill at this cadence, although not found in any of our sources, would be in agreement with the usual baroque performance practice. It may have more repercussions, of course.

PRAELUDIUM 22

Adagio lamentoso ♪ = 60 - 66

BWV 867

ⓐ In the Czerny edition an f¹ is added to the first chord, as on the fourth eighth note. This originates in the old Hoffmeister edition but is not found in any of our sources.

ⓑ The eb¹ is missing from the left hand chord in the Walther ms and in the Czerny edition. In the Altnikol ms, both c¹ and eb¹ are missing.

ⓒ The two f²'s are tied in the Walther, Altnikol, and Schwencke P417 mss. This reading was accepted by Kroll for the Bach-Gesellschaft edition and for his edition for C. F. Peters. It is also found in the Czerny edition. Our text is in agreement with the Autograph and all the other sources.

ⓓ Here Schwencke P417 has, for the two middle voices:

The Gerber ms has the same, except the tenor voice is missing for the entire third beat of the measure.

ⓔ Beginning here the Fischhof ms has:  This version was adopted by Czerny.

(f) In the Kirnberger and both Schwencke mss the two f¹'s and the two e¹'s are tied. The Czerny edition adopted these ties and also ties the corresponding notes in the bass, as well as the two g's in the tenor voice, between the 3rd & 4th beats of the measure. These ties do not appear in the Autograph or the remaining sources.

(g) The natural sign before the a is missing in the Agricola (P202) and Gerber mss and in Schwencke P203. According to Kreutz this is the original version, and the natural was added to the Autograph by Bach as an afterthought.

(h) Here the Walther, Gerber, and Schwencke P203 mss have:

(i) Here the f¹ and g♭¹ of the tenor voice may be taken with the right hand, if preferred.

ⓙ **A trill may be added here, according to the custom of the period:**

FUGA 22

a 5

NB) A slight but definite separation of the two half notes which open the subject is, in the editor's opinion, an effective device for making each entrance clear to the listener, especially in the stretto closing section of this fugue.

(a) In the Czerny edition, the time signature is erroneously **C** instead of **¢**.

ⓑ Instead of e♭¹ the Agricola (P202) and Gerber mss have d♭¹, tied from the previous measure.

ⓒ The Walther ms has f¹ for the alto voice instead of the b♭¹ downstem. The same reading was adopted in the Czerny edition.

(d) There is no flat sign before this c² in the Walther, Agricola, Gerber, or Schwencke P203 mss (probably an older version). It is clearly flat in the Autograph.

(e) Whether this is d♮² or d♭² is controversial. In the Autograph there seems to be a flat sign later changed to a natural. The natural sign is clear in the Agricola (P202), Altnikol, Kirnberger, Fischhof, and Schwencke P417 mss. The Henle, Wiener, and Kreutz "Urtexts" have d♮². The Kroll editions (both the Bach-Gesellschaft and Peters) and the Czerny, Hughes, and Tovey editions have d♭². Busoni offers both readings.

(f) The diagonal lines in dark print, here and in the following two measures, are from the Autograph.

(g) Here Schwencke P203 has:    The Czerny edition, unlike any of our sources, has:

PRAELUDIUM 23

Allegretto tranquillo ♩ = 69-76

BWV 868

ⓐ Here the Walther ms and Schwencke P417 have g♯ instead of the tied-over f double-sharp. Schwencke P203 originally had the same, but it was later corrected.

(b) The following notes were entered over the original version in the Agricola ms (P202). This reading was adopted by Hoffmeister and later by Czerny. The last three notes of this example were also added in the Gerber ms:

For the left hand the Czerny edition has the following, also derived from Hoffmeister:

This reading originally appeared in the Fischhof ms but was later erased and replaced with the version found in the Autograph and in our text.

(c) The tie is missing in the Agricola and Walther mss and in the Czerny edition.

FUGA 23
a 4

BWV 868

NB) The articulation suggested by the editor shows a relationship in the subject matter of this fugue to its prelude. This slight similarity may well be coincidental, and either of the following ideas is just as acceptable:

For additional suggestions see the table on page 216.

ⓐ In the Autograph the trill appears only in the first statement of the fugue subject. It should be added, when practical, each time the theme appears. See the discussion on page 20.

ⓑ This trill appears in the Gerber ms.

ⓒ Here the Henle "Urtext" has an erroneous $c\sharp^1$ instead of b, possibly a typographical error.

ⓓ If a trill is played here a short one is most practical:

ⓔ This trill appears in the Altnikol and both Schwencke mss.

(f) This trill, missing from all our sources, is nevertheless appropriate.

(g) This cadential trill appears in Schwencke P203.

(h) This trill appears in Schwencke P203.

(i) Here the Czerny edition has e♯² instead of e♮².

(j) This trill appears in the Agricola ms (P202).

(k) Both of these trills (measures 30 and 32) are found in Schwencke P203.

PRAELUDIUM 24

NB) The editor suggests that the eighth notes (except those otherwise marked) be played *quasi non legato*. Other notes may be played *legato*. Such articulation brings the treble "duet" into prominence, and the bass assumes the role of accompaniment. Some artists play the left hand *semi-staccato* throughout. Others play both hands *legatissimo*.

ⓐ The tempo indication, *Andante*, is Bach's own.

ⓑ The small ornaments in parentheses may be used when repeating each of the two sections.

ⓒ This trill, not found in our sources, is nevertheless appropriate at this cadence.

ⓓ The Czerny edition has the following erroneous reading, taken from the old Hoffmeister edition:

ⓔ This trill may be played with a termination:

(f) The trills here and in measure 29 and 42 are found in Schwencke P203.

ⓖ The ♯ before the d¹ is missing in the Kirnberger and Gerber mss and in the Czerny edition.

FUGA 24

a 4

(a) The tempo indication, *Largo*, is Bach's own.

(b) In the Busoni edition the time signature is changed to $\frac{4}{2}$, with the remark that Bach's original signature might "tempt the player to undue rapidity."(!)

(c) The slurs in the first statement of the subject appear in the Autograph and all the other sources. They should be understood to apply to all statements of the theme and its inversions. The slurs can hardly function to indicate *notes inégales*, which cannot be consistently applied against the countersubject. They are not merely articulation signs. They do indicate *legato* connections, and as the fugue develops they prove to be written-out *appoggiaturas*. The first of each pair of notes receives the emphasis, and resolves more softly to the second one.

(d) In the Autograph the trill appears only in the first statement of the subject. It may be played, when possible, each time the theme appears. Any measured trill other than one that begins slowly and accelerates, as shown in the realization in light print, is likely to result in consecutive octaves or fifths with the countersubject when it appears in measures 6, 11, 22, etc. See the discussion under ABOUT CONSECUTIVES, on page 19.

(e) Here the Fischhof ms has c♯¹ instead of b. The Autograph seems to have had c♯¹, later changed to b. All our remaining sources have b.

(f) The trill appears in the Altnikol ms.

ⓖ The sharp sign before the d² is missing, not only in the Fischhof ms, but also in the Agricola (P202), Gerber, Walther, and Schwencke P417.

ⓗ For this trill, a termination (turned ending) seems unfunctional.
For simplification a short trill may be used, played:

ⓘ The slurs in dark print are from the Autograph. They appear also in the Agricola and Fischhof mss. The tie between the two d♯¹'s in the Czerny edition is incorrect.

(j) The small staff indicates what Bach presumably would have written had he not limited himself to the range of the smaller keyboard instruments of his day. This has been noted by Kreutz, Keller, Tovey and others.

204

ⓚ A trill on this note seems impractical.

ⓛ The line indicating the voice-leading is from the Autograph.

(m) Here only a short trill is practical, as shown in the realization.
For simplification, the trill may be played:

(n) This trill does not invite the use of a termination (turned ending). For simplification a
short trill may be used, as recommended in footnote (m), above.

○ See footnote ⓙ on page 203.

(p) A trill on the bass note, c, would conform with the use of the trill in the first statement of the subject and answer, but seems quite impractical.

(q) The e♯ is controversial, even though it is present in all of our sources. Some editors have concluded that the sharp sign was crossed out in the Autograph, but this is not clearly so. Kroll (in his editions for Peters and for the Bach-Gesellschaft), Kreutz, the Wiener "Urtext", and Czerny accept the sharp, as we do. Henle, Tovey, Bischoff, Hughes, and Busoni do not.

(r) "S.D.G." = Soli Deo Gloria (to the glory of God alone) and "Fine" are written in Bach's own hand in the Autograph ms.

ARTICULATION TABLES

The information in these tables is derived from commentaries, editions and recordings. Due to space limitations, only the articulation of the subject of each fugue is given.

Few of the artists represented in this table would wish to go on record as endorsing only one particular articulation, since most of these fugues may be effectively articulated a number of different ways. However, the articulation chosen should, in this editor's opinion, be applied consistently each time the subject or answer appears. It is thus important to be sure that the chosen articulation is such that it may be maintained later in the fugue when other voices must be played at the same time with the same hand. A careful testing, while reading through the entire fugue slowly, should be applied to any proposed articulation before a final decision is made. For the countersubject a contrasting articulation is usually most effective, particularly when it helps to define the subject and answer clearly.

Since it is difficult to be incontestably accurate in transcribing some of the more subtle elements of articulation from phonograph recordings, the editor was not content to use only the evidence of his own ears, but was assisted by several other professional musicians in arriving at the indications printed here. It is, of course, not practical to attempt to indicate all the subtle devices of dynamics that are so often skillfully employed by artists to make the basic articulation much more effective.

Some of the artists whose recordings were used in preparing these tables are exemplary with regard to consistency, while others are not. In several instances the subject seems to be articulated differently with each appearance. In such cases the articulation given in the table is that of the opening statement, except in a few instances where some other articulation seems to predominate as the fugue progresses. In the latter case the table shows the articulation most frequently used.

In studying these tables, the reader may wish to review the remarks in the foreword under PHRASING AND ARTICULATION (pp. 24-26).

FUGUE NO. 1 IN C MAJOR

BISCHOFF, GOULD, GULDA, FISCHER, MARTINS, RICHTER, TURECK:

legato
Martins: poco marcato.

BODKY, GALLING, HAMILTON, KELLER:

BUSONI:

mf

CZERNY:

p sempre legato

DEMUS, KIRKPATRICK:

DOLMETSCH:

HUGHES:

poco f (legato)

LANDOWSKA: *(Original version. See p. 7)*

legato

LEONHARDT:

NEWMAN:

FUGUE NO. 2 IN C MINOR

BISCHOFF, HAMILTON:

BODKY:

BUSONI:

p

CZERNY:

pp

DEMUS, HUGHES:
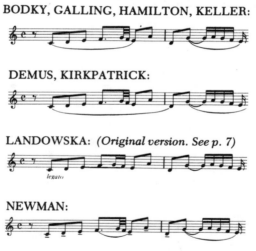
Hughes: p

FISCHER, LANDOWSKA:

Fischer: almost no break between slurs.

GALLING:

GOULD:

GULDA:

FUGUE NO. 2 IN C MINOR (continued)

FUGUE NO. 3 IN C♯ MAJOR

FUGUE NO. 4 IN C♯ MINOR

FUGUE NO. 5 IN D MAJOR

210

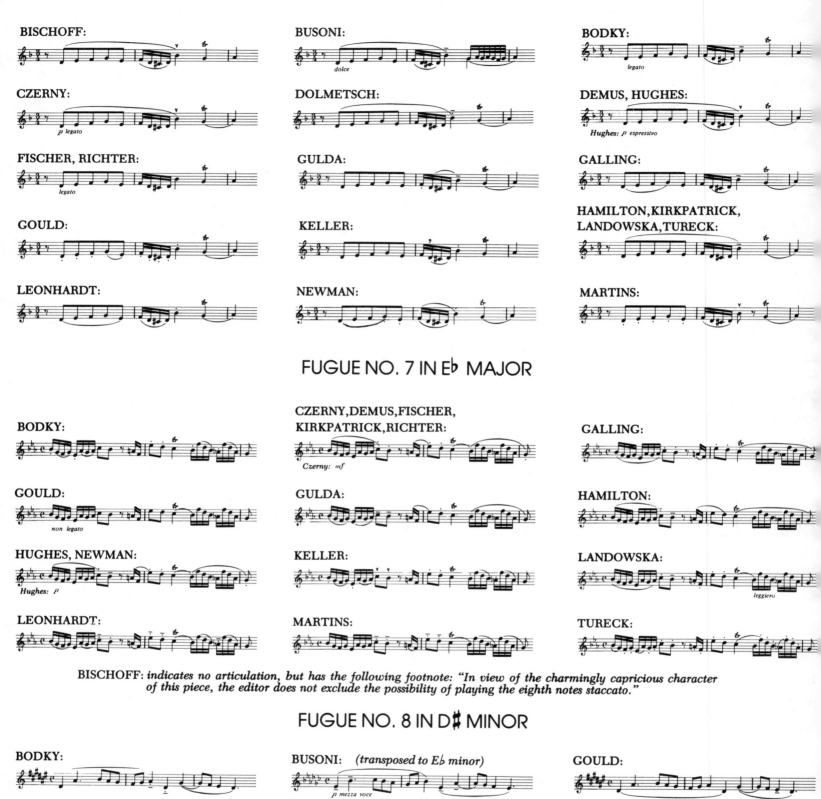

BISCHOFF: *indicates no articulation, but has the following footnote: "In view of the charmingly capricious character of this piece, the editor does not exclude the possibility of playing the eighth notes staccato."*

FUGUE NO. 8 IN D♯ MINOR

FUGUE NO. 9 IN E MAJOR

BODKY, GOULD: *leggiero*

BUSONI: *f < non legato, vivamente*

DEMUS:

FISCHER: *quasi legato*

GALLING:

GULDA: *detached*

HAMILTON:

KIRKPATRICK, MARTINS, NEWMAN, RICHTER:

LANDOWSKA:

LEONHARDT:

TURECK:

BISCHOFF: tranquillo. No articulation marks.
CZERNY: The first 2 notes slurred. No further indications.
HUGHES: upbeat staccato, quarter note accented. No further indications.
KELLER: "Upbeat staccato." No further remarks.

FUGUE NO. 10 IN E MINOR

BISCHOFF: *leggiero, ma ben accentuato*

BODKY: *leggiero*

BUSONI: *f non legato, distintamente*

CZERNY, FISCHER, KIRKPATRICK, TURECK: *Czerny: p ——— sf*

DOLMETSCH: *(distinctly articulated)*

GALLING, HUGHES: *Hughes: f non legato*

GOULD, GULDA: *leggiero*

HAMILTON:

KELLER: *non legato*

KIRKPATRICK:

LANDOWSKA:

LEONHARDT:

MARTINS: *(distinctly detached)*

NEWMAN:

RICHTER:

FUGUE NO. 11 IN F MAJOR

BODKY: *legato*

BUSONI: *mezza voce*

CZERNY: *p*

DEMUS, KIRKPATRICK:

FISCHER, KELLER:

GALLING:

GOULD:

HAMILTON:

HUGHES: *mf*

LANDOWSKA:

LEONHARDT:

MARTINS: *(quasi legato)*

RICHTER:

TURECK:

NEWMAN:

GULDA: marcato, all notes detached (on the 1st statement of the subject.)

BISCHOFF: tranquillo. No articulation indicated.

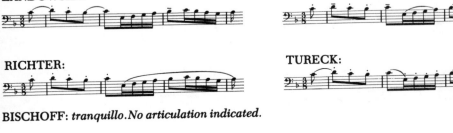

FUGUE NO. 12 IN F MINOR

BODKY:

molto legato

BUSONI, FISCHER, KIRKPATRICK:

Busoni: p ben tenuto

CZERNY,DEMUS,GALLING,GULDA, KELLER, LANDOWSKA,HAMILTON MARTINS,TURECK,RICHTER:

Czerny: p *legato*

GOULD:

HUGHES:

p ben tenuto

LEONHARDT, NEWMAN:

BISCHOFF: *legato e pensieroso. No articulation indicated.*

FUGUE NO. 13 IN F♯ MAJOR

BUSONI:

dolce

BODKY,DEMUS, FISCHER, GULDA,HAMILTON, HUGHES, LANDOWSKA,MARTINS,RICHTER:

Hughes: p

CZERNY:

p   *p*

GOULD:

GALLING:

KELLER:

LEONHARDT:

KIRKPATRICK:

NEWMAN:

BISCHOFF: *amabile. No articulation marked.*

TURECK:

FUGUE NO. 14 IN F♯ MINOR

BODKY,FISCHER, GALLING,GULDA,HAMILTON KIRKPATRICK,LANDOWSKA, MARTINS,RICHTER,TURECK:

legato

BUSONI:

mf molto tenuto

CZERNY:

mf legato ed espressivo   *sf dimin.*

GOULD:

KELLER, NEWMAN:

LEONHARDT:

(very subtle slurring, quasi molto legato)

BISCHOFF, HUGHES: *No articulation indicated.*

FUGUE NO. 15 IN G MAJOR

BISCHOFF, CZERNY:

Bischoff: vivo
Czerny: p the quarter notes accented.

BODKY:

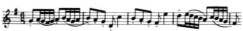

DEMUS,FISCHER,HUGHES, MARTINS,RICHTER:

Hughes: mp

GALLING:

GOULD:

(lightly detached, except as marked.)

GULDA, TURECK:

HAMILTON:

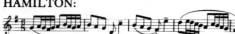

KELLER:

KIRKPATRICK:

(quasi legato)

LANDOWSKA:

LEONHARDT:

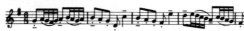

NEWMAN:

FUGUE NO. 16 IN G MINOR

BODKY:

f   *leggiero*

BUSONI:

*poco f nobilmente espressivo,
un poco pesante*

CZERNY:

mf

DEMUS:

**FISCHER, GOULD, GULDA, HAMILTON,
HUGHES, LANDOWSKA, MARTINS,
TURECK, RICHTER:**

Hughes: mf

GALLING:

KELLER:

KIRKPATRICK:

LEONHARDT:

BISCHOFF: *molto tranquillo.*
  No articulation indicated.

NEWMAN:

FUGUE NO. 17 IN A♭ MAJOR

BISCHOFF, HUGHES:

both: tranquillo e con espressione.
Bischoff: no articulation suggested.
Hughes: sempre legato

BODKY, MARTINS: *legato e portato*

Martins: marcato

BUSONI:

mf

CZERNY:

p sempre legato e pesante

**DEMUS, FISCHER, GALLING, GULDA,
HAMILTON, KELLER, KIRKPATRICK,
LANDOWSKA, RICHTER, TURECK:**

GOULD:

LEONHARDT:

NEWMAN:

FUGUE NO. 18 IN G♯ MINOR

BODKY:

portato

BUSONI:

non f   *quasi stacc.*

CZERNY, LANDOWSKA:

Czerny: f   *p*

FISCHER, GOULD, TURECK:

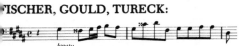

legato

GALLING, GULDA, RICHTER:

HAMILTON:

HUGHES:

p espressivo

KELLER:

"legato. Repeated notes lightly separated."

LEONHARDT:

BISCHOFF: *espressivo.*
  No articulation indicated.

MARTINS:

FUGUE NO. 19 IN A MAJOR

BODKY:

BUSONI:

flexibly

sotto voce, dolcemente

CZERNY:

ff   *p*   *p*

DEMUS, FISCHER:

GALLING, HAMILTON:

GOULD:

GULDA, LEONHARDT, TURECK:

HUGHES:

f   *p*

KIRKPATRICK, MARTINS, RICHTER:

legato

KELLER:

"or the subject may be slurred throughout."

LANDOWSKA:

NEWMAN:

BISCHOFF: *No articulation indicated.*

FUGUE NO. 20 IN A MINOR

BISCHOFF:

BODKY:

non legato   *"più legato only for the beautiful episode, bars 40-42."*

BUSONI:

mf   *non legato*

CZERNY:

p   *cresc.*   *f*   *p*

DEMUS:

FISCHER:

GALLING:

GOULD

GULDA:

molto marcato

HAMILTON:

HUGHES:

mf

KELLER:

KIRKPATRICK:

LANDOWSKA:

LEONHARDT:

MARTINS:

NEWMAN:

RICHTER:

TURECK:

FUGUE NO. 21 IN B♭ MAJOR

FUGUE NO. 22 IN B♭ MINOR

FUGUE NO. 23 IN B MAJOR

BODKY:

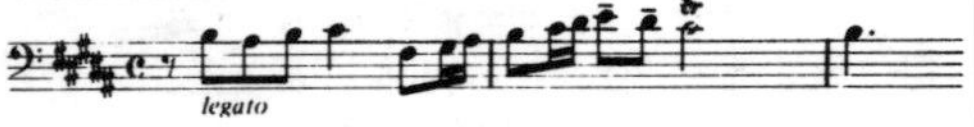
legato

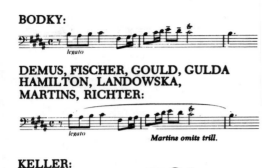

DEMUS, FISCHER, GOULD, GULDA HAMILTON, LANDOWSKA, MARTINS, RICHTER:

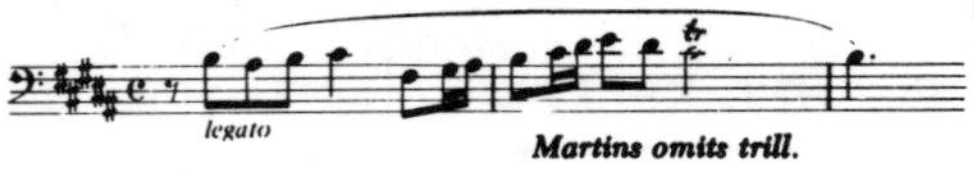
legato
Martins omits trill.

KELLER:

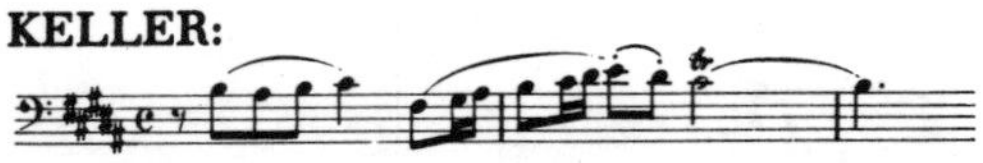

BISCHOFF: *cantabile.*
No articulation indicated.

BUSONI: *dolce, ma serioso*

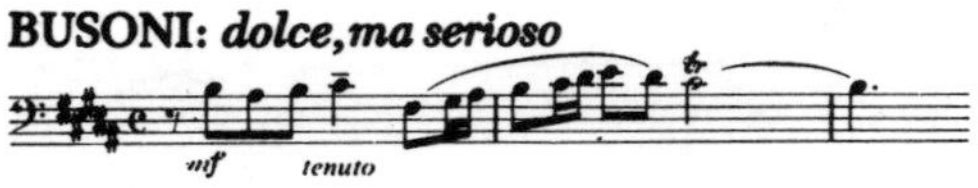
mf
tenuto

GALLING:

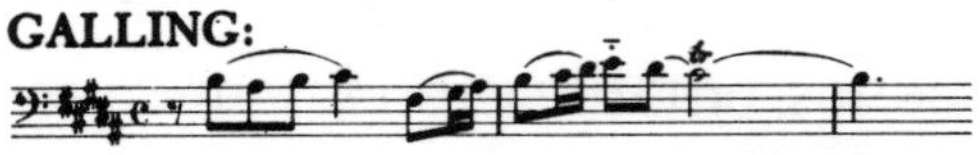

KIRKPATRICK:

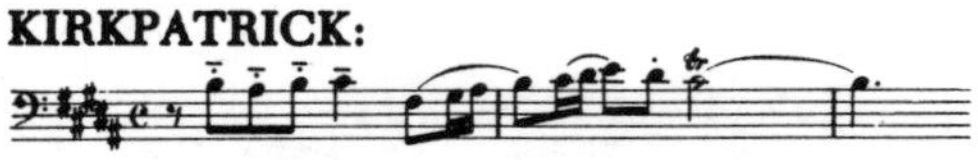

NEWMAN:

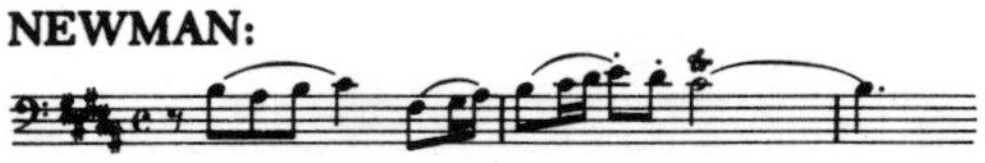

CZERNY:

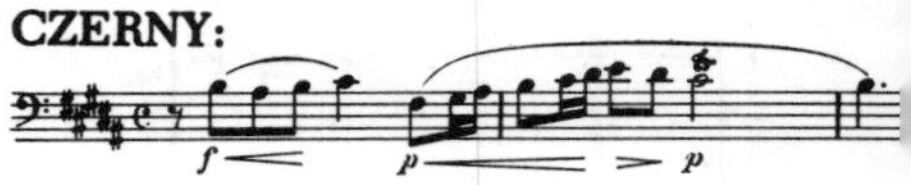
f
p
p

HUGHES:

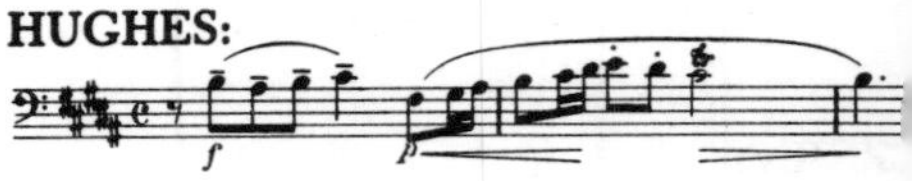
f
p

LEONHARDT:

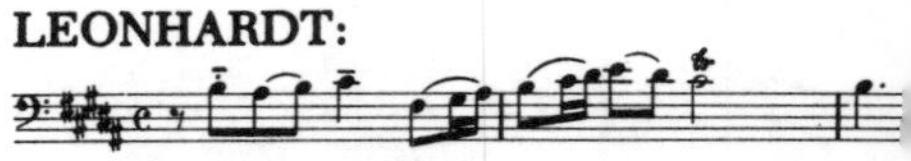

TURECK:

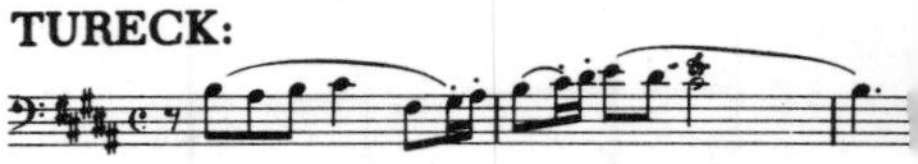

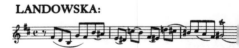

FUGUE NO. 24 IN B MINOR

BISCHOFF:

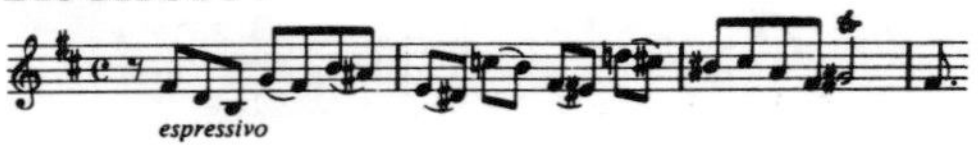
espressivo

CZERNY:

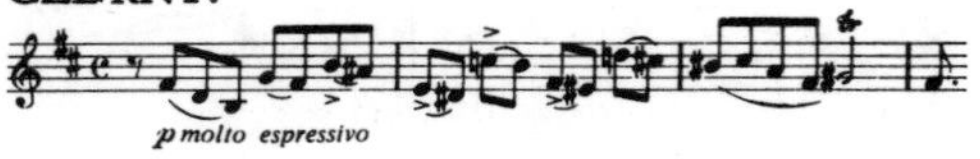
p molto espressivo

GOULD:

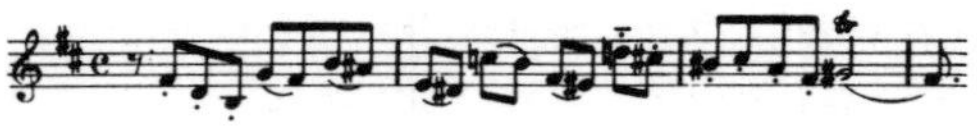

KELLER:

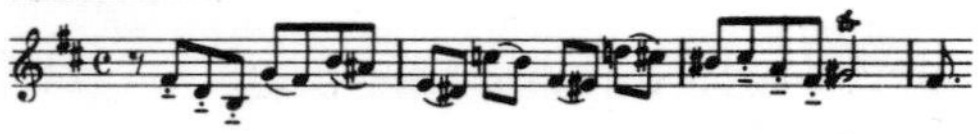

LEONHARDT:

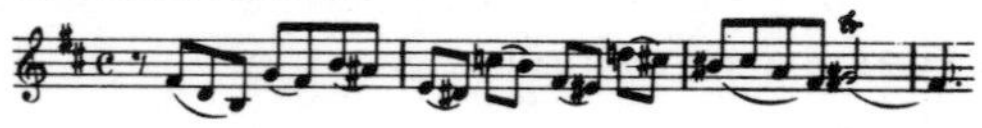

BODKY:

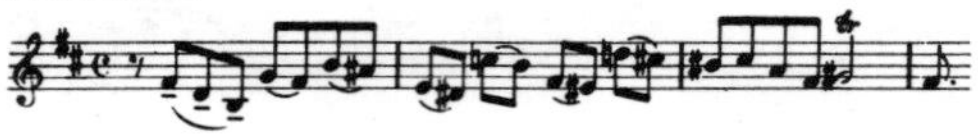

DEMUS:

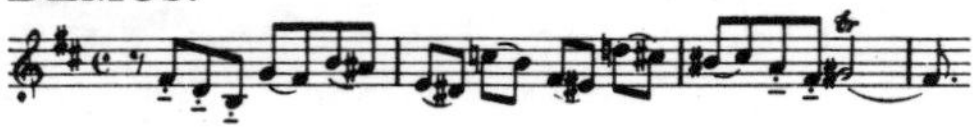

GULDA, FISCHER:

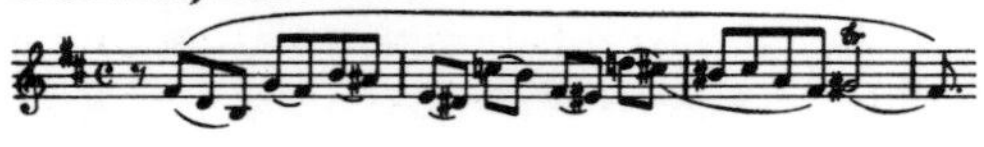

KIRKPATRICK:

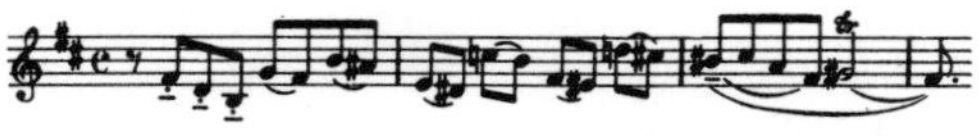

MARTINS:

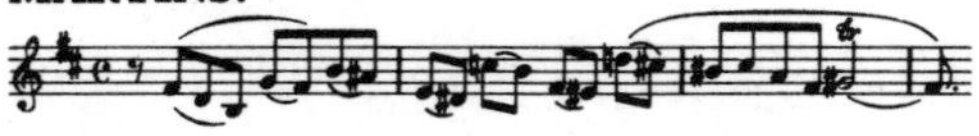

TURECK:

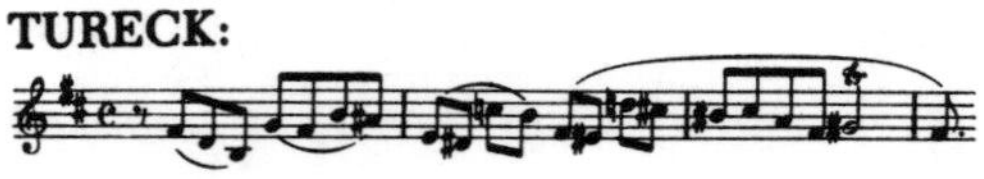

BUSONI:

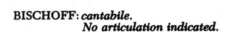

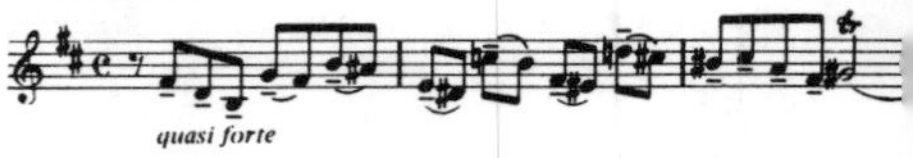
quasi forte

GALLING, HUGHES, RICHTER:

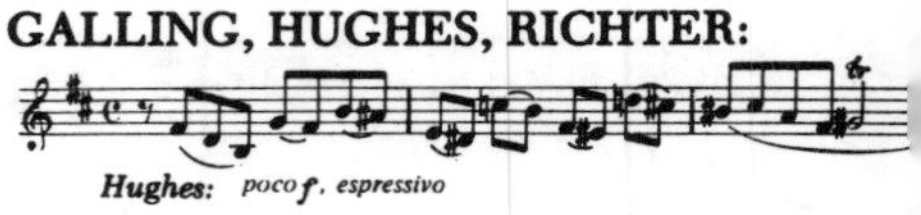
Hughes: poco f. espressivo

HAMILTON:

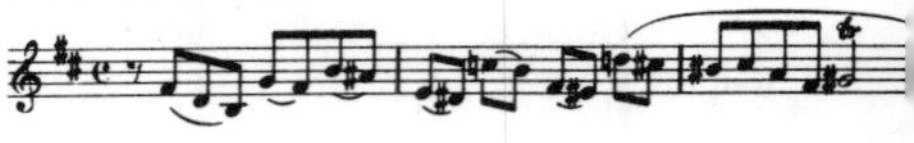

LANDOWSKA:

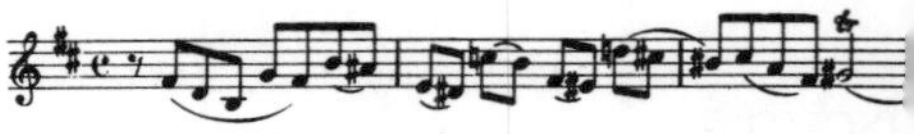

NEWMAN:

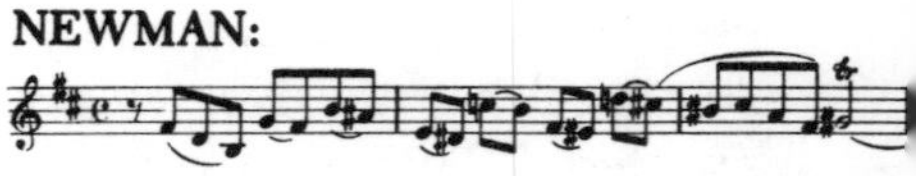

RECORDINGS

The recordings listed below were used in tabulating the articulation tables on the preceding pages and the approximate metronomic tempo indications on the following pages.

Johann Sebastian Bach, *THE WELL-TEMPERED CLAVIER, VOL.I;* Joerg Demus, Piano (Westminster W9332/3).

J. S. Bach, Recording by Arnold Dolmetsch: see note at the bottom of this list.

Jean-Sebastien Bach, *LE CLAVIER BIEN TEMPÉRÉ, LIVRE 1,* Edwin Fischer, Piano (Les Gravures Illustres 2C 061-01300/1).

Bach, *THE WELL-TEMPERED CLAVIER, BOOK I;* Martin Galling, Harpsichord (Vox SVBX 5436).

Bach, *THE WELL-TEMPERED CLAVIER, BOOK I COMPLETE;* Glenn Gould, Piano (Columbia D35573).

Johann Sebastian Bach, *DAS WOHLTEMPERIERTE KLAVIER, ERSTER TEIL,* Friedrich Gulda, Piano (MPS 4921551-0).

Bach, *THE WELL-TEMPERED CLAVIER, BOOKS 1 & 2;* Malcom Hamilton, Harpsichord (Everest 3134/6).

J. S. Bach, *DAS WOHLTEMPERIERTE KLAVIER, 1. TEIL;* Ralph Kirkpatrick, Harpsichord (Deutsche Grammophon LPM 18 844/45).

J. S. Bach, *THE WELL-TEMPERED CLAVIER, BOOK I;* Wanda Landowska, Harpsichord (RCA VCM-6203).

J. S. Bach, *LE CLAVIER BIEN TEMPÉRÉ, 1ère ET 2ème PARTIES;* Gustav Leonhardt, Harpsichord (Harmonia Mundi/HM 20309-13).

J. S. Bach, *THE WELL-TEMPERED CLAVIER, BOOK I,* João Carlos Martins, Piano (Connoisseur Society CS 2014, 2025 & 2043).

J. S. Bach, *THE WELL-TEMPERED CLAVIER, BOOK I;* Anthony Newman, Harpsichord (Columbia M2 32500).

J. S. Bach, *THE WELL-TEMPERED CLAVIER, BOOK I;* Sviatoslav Richter, Piano (Melodiya/Angel SRC 4119).

Bach, *THE WELL-TEMPERED CLAVIER, BOOK I;* Rosalyn Tureck, Piano (Decca DL710120/22).

The clavichord recording of Arnold Dolmetsch, commissioned by 'The 48 Society', was made by the Columbia Gramophone Company in 1934, when Dolmetsch was nearing his 76th birthday. The project was to have included all 48 preludes and fugues in the two volumes of *The Well-Tempered Clavier,* plus the *Chromatic Fantasia.* From volume 1 Dolmetsch recorded only preludes and fugues numbers 1, 5, 6, 10, 21, and 22. From volume 2 he recorded numbers 1, 7, 12, and 15. He also recorded the *Chromatic Fantasia.* The recording is exceedingly rare, and the editor is deeply indebted to Arnold Dolmetsch's distinguished son, Dr. Carl Dolmetsch, for kind permission to use a tape recording made from one of the original pressings, and for so thoughtfully providing same.

The recording was made under extremely trying circumstances. Arnold Dolmetsch suffered an automobile accident on the way to the recording studio for the first session. In spite of this and other difficulties, reviewers were enthusiastic in their praise of the results. Dolmetsch's use of *notes inégales,* overdotting, and other baroque devices, was accepted by the most distinguished critics, including Ernest Newman, who commented that Dolmetsch's extensive research had led him to "certain conclusions the general truth of which cannot be disputed." This is surprising for the year 1934, and we must remember that these same conclusions were published in 1915.

SELECT BIBLIOGRAPHY

This list includes only books published in English.

Bach, Carl Philip Emanuel. ESSAY ON THE TRUE ART OF PLAYING KEYBOARD INSTRUMENTS. First published in German. Part I in 1753, part II in 1762, in Berlin. English translation by W. J. Mitchell, W. W. Norton & Co., New York, 1949.

Bodky, Erwin. THE INTERPRETATION OF BACH'S KEYBOARD WORKS. Harvard University Press, Cambridge, Massachusetts, 1960.

Couperin, Francois. L'ART DE TOUCHER LE CLAVECIN. First published in French, in Paris, 1716. Newly edited and translated by Margery Halford, Alfred Publishing Co., Sherman Oaks, California, 1974.

David, Hans T. & Mendel, Arthur. THE BACH READER, A LIFE OF JOHANN SEBASTIAN BACH IN LETTERS AND DOCUMENTS. W. W. Norton & Co., New York, 1945. Revised ed., 1966.

(Continued on page 220)

One of the difficulties in preparing this table of metronomic indications is that almost no artist chooses to maintain a steady tempo throughout any of these pieces. Several of the preludes have a character of free improvisation, and these are particularly problematical. Irwin Bodky's idea of using round numbers for all metronomic tempos, with the words "plus-or-minus" appended, is practical, at least when applied to one section of a piece played by one artist.

The wide divergence of supposedly knowlegeable opinion represented by this table could be the subject of a long discussion. Prelude No. 24 is a particularly interesting example. Compare Malcolm Hamilton's ♩ = 40 with Glenn Gould's ♩ = 84 and with Anthony Newmann's ♩ = 132! The present editor would be the last to say that any of these tempos is wrong.

It is well to remember that tempos may vary with factors other than the taste and moods of the individual, including the responsiveness and tonal clarity of a particular instrument, as well as the acoustics and resonance of a room or hall. It was completely in the baroque spirit to leave the choice of tempo to the performer.

Busoni is omitted from this table because he did not supply metronomic indications in his edition.

Since Arnold Dolmetsch recorded only six of the Preludes and Fugues, his tempos are compiled separately in the table below.

RECORDING BY CLAVICHORDIST Arnold Dolmetsch		
No. 1.	Prelude	♩ = 120
	Fugue	♩ = 60
No. 5.	Prelude	♩ = 120
	Fugue	♩ = 63
No. 6.	Prelude	♩ = 66-69
	Fugue	♩ = 60
No. 10.	Prelude	♩ = 48
	M.23	♩ = 92
	Fugue	♩ = 69-72
No. 21.	Prelude	♩ = 72
	Fugue	♩ = 76
No. 22.	Prelude	♪ = 66
	Fugue	♩ = 96

Abbreviations:

N/I = no indications.

pr = previous section. ♩ = ♪ pr means "a quarter note is equal to an eighth note of the previous section."

r = ritarding to. ♩ = 84r 63 means "beginning at ♩ = 84 and ritarding to ♩ = 63.

TABLE OF TEMPO INDICATIONS

No.		COMMENTARIES		EDITIONS				
		Keller	Bodky	Czerny	Bischoff	Mugellini	Hughes	Bartok
No. 1.	Prelude	♩= 72	♩= ±80	♩= 112	♩= 112	♩= 108	♩= 112	♩= 88-92
	Fugue	♩= 54-58	♩= ±60	♪= 116	♩= 63	♩= 66	♩= 60	♩= 66-69
No. 2.	Prelude	♩= 84	♩= ±120	♩= 144	♩= 108	♩= 120	♩= 132	♩= 116
	M.28	♩= 126	N/I	N/I	♩= 126	N/I	♩= 144	♩= 140
	M.34	♪= 63	N/I	N/I	N/I	N/I	N/I	N/I
	M.35	♩= 84 r 63	N/I	N/I	N/I	N/I	♪=♪ pr	N/I
	Fugue	♩= 63	♩= ±80	♩= 80	♩= 80	♩= 80	♩= 80	♩= 80-88
No. 3.	Prelude	♩.= 84-92	♩.= ±60	♩.= 92	♩.= 84	♩.= 92	♩.= 84	♩.= 84
	Fugue	♩= 84-92	♩= ±80	♩= 104	♩= 100	♩= 96	♩= 96	♩= 92
No. 4.	Prelude	𝅗𝅥.= 40	𝅗𝅥.= ±40	♩= 92	♩= 92	♩= 92	♩= 96	♩= 108
	Fugue	𝅗𝅥= 58-63	𝅝= ±80	♩= 112	♩= 100	♩= 100	𝅝= 48	𝅗𝅥= 60
No. 5.	Prelude	♩= 96	♩= ±120	♩= 132	♩= 132	♩= 126	♩= 138	♩= 138
	Fugue	♩= 63-66	♩= ±60	♩= 76	♩= 80	♩= 69	♩= 60	♩= 60
No. 6.	Prelude	♩= 52 r 36	♩= ±60	♩= 80	♩= 76	♩= 84	♩= 80	♩= 70
	Fugue	♩= 72	♩= ±80	♩= 66	♩= 72	♩= 72	♩= 72	♩= 69
No. 7.	Prelude	♩= 60	♩= ±80	♩= 80	♩= 69	♩= 76	♩= 72	♩= 88
	M.10	N/I	N/I	N/I	N/I	♩= 69	N/I	N/I
	M.25	N/I	N/I	N/I	N/I	♩= 80	N/I	N/I
	Fugue	♩= 84-92	♩= ±80	♩= 112	♩= 104	♩= 96	♩= 88	♩= 96
No. 8.	Prelude	𝅗𝅥= 44	𝅗𝅥= 50	♩= 100	𝅗𝅥= 50	𝅗𝅥= 42	𝅗𝅥= 50	♩= 72
	Fugue	♩= 60-66	♩= ±80	♩= 76	♩= 72	♩= 72	♩= 72	♩= 72
No. 9.	Prelude	♩.= 63-69	♩.= ±80	♩.= 84	♩.= 92	♩.= 88	♩.= 84	♩.= 70-76
	Fugue	♩= 96-104	♩= ±100	♩= 108	♩= 116	♩= 108	♩= 104	♩= 100
No. 10.	Prelude	♩= 58-63	♩= ±60	♩= 84	♩= 69	♩= 69	♩= 66	♩= 54-60
	M.23	♩= 116-126	♩= ±120	𝅗𝅥= 80	N/I	♩= 120	♩= 132	𝅗𝅥= 54-60
	Fugue	♩= 116-126	♩= ±120	♩= 126	♩= 132	♩= 126	♩= 116	♩= 116
No. 11.	Prelude	♩.= 76-84	♩.= ±60	♩.= 88	♩.= 80	♩.= 76	♩.= 80	♩.= 80
	Fugue	♩.= 50-54	♩.= ±60	♩.= 66	♩.= 60	♩.= 60	♩.= 54	♩.= 66
No. 12.	Prelude	♩= 48-56	♩= ±60	♪= 104	♩= 56	♩= 52	♩= 52	♩= 63
	Fugue	♩= 48-56	♩= ±60	♩= 63	♩= 66	♩= 66	♩= 63	♩= 60
No. 13.	Prelude	♪.= 84-92	♪.= ±60	♪.= 96	♪.= 104	♪.= 104	♪.= 96	♪.= 84
	Fugue	♩= 63-69	♩= ±80	♩= 88	♩= 76	♩= 76	♩= 76	♩= 76
No. 14.	Prelude	♩= 84	♩= ±80	♩= 100	♩= 108	♩= 104	♩= 92	♩= 108
	Fugue	♩= 96	𝅗𝅥= ±40	♩= 88	♩= 100	♩= 100	♩= 84	♩= 94-100
No. 15.	Prelude	♩= 80	♩= ±60	♩= 100	♩= 96	♩= 96	♩= 96	♩= 80
	Fugue	♩.= 66-72	♩.= ±60	♩.= 80	♩.= 76	♩.= 69	♩.= 66	♩.= 60
No. 16.	Prelude	♩= 44	♩= ±60	♩= 69	♩= 56	♪= 92	♩= 50	♩= 56
	Fugue	♩= 56	♩= ±80	♩= 80	♩= 80	♩= 60	♩= 60	♩= 80
No. 17.	Prelude	♩= 72	♩= ±80	♩= 96	♩= 108	♩= 108	♩= 100	N/I
	Fugue	♩= 44-48	♩= ±60	♩= 60	♩= 60	♩= 66	♩= 60	N/I
No. 18.	Prelude	♪= 96	♩.= ±60	♪= 126	♪= 132	♪= 132	♪= 120	♩.= 46
	Fugue	♩= 63	♩= ±60	♪= 108	♩= 56	♩= 60	♩= 56	♩= 66-69
No. 19.	Prelude	♩= 66	♩= ±80	♩= 80	♩= 84	♩= 80	♩= 76	♩= 92
	Fugue	♩.= 66	♩.= ±60	♩.= 69	♩.= 66	♩.= 66	♩.= 66	♩.= 54-60
No. 20.	Prelude	♩.= 66	♩.= 60	♩.= 84	♩.= 80	♩.= 80	♩.= 88	♩.= 84
	Fugue	♩= 66	♩= ±80	♩= 72	♩= 66	♩= 66	♩= 69	♩= 72
No. 21.	Prelude	♩= 69	♩= ±80	♩= 84	♩= 76	♩= 76	♩= 80	♩= 76
	Fugue	♩= 96	♩= ±100	♩= 116	♩= 120	♩= 104	♩= 96	♩= 84
No. 22.	Prelude	♩= 50-54	♩= ±40	♪= 92	♪= 92	♪= 84	♪= 76	♪= 92
	Fugue	𝅗𝅥= 50-54	𝅗𝅥= ±60	𝅗𝅥= 60	♩= 104	♩= 104	𝅗𝅥= 52	𝅗𝅥= 60
No. 23.	Prelude	♩= 72-80	♩= ±80	♩= 76	♩= 80	♩= 80	♩= 80	N/I
	Fugue	♩= 60	♩= ±60	♪= 126	♩= 60	♩= 60	♩= 60	N/I
No. 24.	Prelude	♩= 69	♩= ±80	♩= 80	♩= 69	♩= 76	♩= 72	𝅗𝅥= 58
	Fugue	♩= 48-54	♩= ±40	♪= 92	♩= 52	♩= 52	♩= 46	♩= 46

RECORDINGS BY PIANISTS							RECORDINGS BY HARPSICHORDISTS							
Demus	Fischer	Gould	Gulda	Martins	Richter	Tureck	Galling	Hamilton	Kirkpatrick	Landowska	Leonhardt	Newman		
69	96	60	69	72	72	52	63	58	80	60	84	84	Prelude	No. 1.
48	69	58	72	88	46	44	60	63	58	66	58	69	Fugue	
120	132	80	63	132	132	108	66	120	104	112	96	80	Prelude	No. 2.
144	144	freely	132	144	144	144	132	120	144	126	112	144	M.28	
44	42	freely	40	66	freely	freely	48	freely	freely	112	72	52	M.34	
freely	120	freely	112	112	132	88r40	63	104	±104	92	96	78	M.35	
69	72	88	60	88	84	69	66	76	80	72	66	84	Fugue	
88	80	104	88	104	88	84	72	84	92	92	66	96	Prelude	No. 3.
100	92	104	96	96	104	84	84	84	104	96	66	100	Fugue	
92	84	96	132	92	78	72	88	76	96	76-88	84	108	Prelude	No. 4.
46	46	69	56	72	72	46	120	42	63	40	104	60	Fugue	
132	132	160	132	144	144	108	112	132	120	120	96	132	Prelude	No. 5.
60	60	69	54	60	60	48	63	60	63	63	56	68	Fugue	
72	80	88	84	76	72	80	66	72	84	72	60	84	Prelude	No. 6.
52	63	84	60	84	56	48	69	72	72	76	60	90	Fugue	
69	80	69	84	56	88	54	76	56	112	50	63	69	Prelude	No. 7.
72	63	60	72	50	66	66	76	58	96	72	60	84	M.10	
72	84	88	80	48	84	60	76	52	104	48	60	72	M.25	
90	92	92	92	84	104	76	88	76	96	88	60	92	Fugue	
72	40	72	60	52	58	50	72	46	80	46	48	69	Prelude	No. 8.
69	60	72	60	69	56	58	66	48	84	52	52	84	Fugue	
72	96	63	72	63	96	60	69	69	72	66	66	84	Prelude	No. 9.
100	96	112	112	104	104	84	80	80	104	84	72	96	Fugue	
42	63	46	56	76	69	40	50	40	76	44	66	54	Prelude	No. 10.
132	132	92	120	112-120	120	120	112	104	144	104	104	120	M.23	
96	104	132	120	112	102	69	80	80	84	104	92	116	Fugue	
72	96	80	80	76	80	69	54	66	84	63	48	66	Prelude	No. 11.
58	58	60	63	54	60	58	48	60	60	60	44	60	Fugue	
56	60	40	56	66	46	44	46	40	48	40	44	42	Prelude	No. 12.
56	52	72	44	40	46	54	56	46	48	40	48	66	Fugue	
72	120	56	72	69	92	69	88	84	104	84	80	96	Prelude	No. 13.
56	72	66	60	52	66	69	63	69	88	80	56	84	Fugue	
96	112	104	112	120	120	76	80	80	80	80	66	88	Prelude	No. 14.
72	63	63	58	80	56	66	72	50	80	54	84	112	Fugue	
88	96	104	88	104	88	84	80	80	88	72	66	90	Prelude	No. 15.
66	69	76	69	66	76	60	58	58	58	58	58	63	Fugue	
78	72	72	54	40	92	42	44	66	63	80	96	42	Prelude	No. 16
69	69	63	52	52	52	50	72	56	80	69	54	92	Fugue	
80	88	96	88	112	112	88	84	104	84	84	80	96	Prelude	No. 17.
60	66	96	48	66	50	63	58	44	69	46	69	50	Fugue	
112	112	120	112	96	132	44	96	112	120	112	100	160	Prelude	No. 18.
54	52	92	63	66	96	48	58	60	63	60	52	84	Fugue	
96	88	96	120	76	84	66	80	72	76	63	60	80	Prelude	No. 19.
56	88	69	96	63	63	54	88	72	80	58	76	79	Fugue	
80	92	72	76	104	92	72	63	72	56	63	80	76	Prelude	No. 20.
63	84	104	80	56	84	72	58	72	80	76	69	82	Fugue	
76	96	88	84	84	88	80	72	76	72	69	72	76	Prelude	No. 21.
96	96	104	112	76	96	69	84	72	84	80	76	88	Fugue	
69	60	42	60	69	42	66	40	76	42	66	44	72	Prelude	No. 22.
44	92	69	48	96	72	46	56	46	60	76	54	66	Fugue	
66	66	84	76	92	96	63	63	63	76	42	54	69	Prelude	No. 23.
54	52	84	40	63	54	60	60	66	84	63	52	74	Fugue	
72	66	84	44	69	52	69	69	40	84	69	96	132	Prelude	No. 24.
50	46	80	76	60	76	42	72	54	56	66	42	80	Fugue	

SELECT BIBLIOGRAPHY
(Continued from page 217)

Donington, Robert. THE INTERPRETATION OF EARLY MUSIC. St. Martin's Press, New York, 1974.

Ferguson, Howard, KEYBOARD INTERPRETATION. Oxford University Press, New York & London

Ferguson, Howard. KEYBOARD INTERPRETATION FROM THE 14th TO THE 19th CENTURY. Oxford University Press, New York & London, 1975.

Jorgensen, Owen. TUNING THE HISTORICAL TEMPERAMENTS BY EAR. Northern Michigan University Press, Marquette, 1977.

Keller, Hermann. PHRASING AND ARTICULATION, A CONTRIBUTION TO THE RHETORIC OF MUSIC. First published in German in 1953. English translation by Leigh Gerdine, W. W. Norton & Co., New York, 1965.

Keller, Hermann. THE WELL-TEMPERED CLAVIER BY J. S. BACH. First Published in German in 1965. English translation by Leigh Gerdine, W. W. Norton & Co., 1976.

Landowska, Wanda. LANDOWSKA ON MUSIC. Collected, edited and translated by Denise Restout and Robert Hawkins, Stein and Day, New York, 1964.

Palmer, Willard A., & Halford, Margery. THE BAROQUE ERA, AN INTRODUCTION TO THE KEYBOARD MUSIC. Alfred Publishing Co., Inc., Sherman Oaks, California, 1976.

Quantz, Johann Joachim. ON PLAYING THE FLUTE. First published in German, Berlin, 1752. English translation by Edward R. Reilly, Faber & Faber, London, 1966.

ACKNOWLEDGMENTS

For kind permission to use research materials such as manuscripts, early editions, photocopies and microfilms, I am indebted to: The Staatsbibliothek (Preussischer Kulturbesitz), Musikabteilung, Berlin; The Riemenschneider Bach Institute (Baldwin-Wallace College), Berea, Ohio; The Yale University Music Library, New Haven, Connecticut; The Music Library of the University of Houston; The Music Library of Rice University, Houston; The British Library, London.

For personal assistance in preparing this edition, including those who contributed many hours of assistance and those who provided important bits of information, helpful suggestions or constructive criticisms, I wish to thank: Elinore Barber, Heskell Brisman, William Conte, Carl Dolmetsch, Rudolf Elvers, Margery Halford, Judith Heiss, Judith and Arthur Howard (my daughter and son-in-law), Juanita Hubbard, Owen Jorgensen, Michael Keach, Amanda Vick Lethco, John O'Reilly, Thomas Palmer and Willard Palmer III (my sons), Larry Palmer (unfortunately not a relative), Mary Schoettle and Benjamin Suchoff.

A very special acknowledgement is due to Judith Schneider, whose assistance with the tedious research for this edition spanned a period of ten years. A sample of her careful notes may be seen in the facsimile of her worksheets on page 6.

Special thanks are due to Iris and Morton Manus, the guiding spirits and geniuses behind Alfred Publishing Company, who seem to me to be family members rather than business associates. Their faith in my work, their support of my research, their patience with my idiosyncracies, their unfailing encouragement, and their high standards regarding the production and promotion of our editions have made the realization of this work possible, and have enabled me to maintain high standards in the execution of it.

And to my dear wife, Ruby Touchstone Palmer, the most patient and enduring of all, who has always endeavored to make my work as pleasant and as free of other cares as possible, no amount of thanks can suffice.

Willard A. Palmer